THE GARBAGE KING

Elizabeth Laird

adapted by Oladipo Agboluaje

OXFORD
UNIVERSITY PRESS

Great Clarendon Street, Oxford OX2 6DP

Oxford University Press is a department of the University of Oxford.
It furthers the University's objective of excellence in research,
scholarship, and education by publishing worldwide in

Oxford   New York

Auckland   Cape Town   Dar es Salaam   Hong Kong   Karachi
Kuala Lumpur   Madrid   Melbourne   Mexico City   Nairobi
New Delhi   Shanghai   Taipei   Toronto

With offices in

Argentina   Austria   Brazil   Chile   Czech Republic   France   Greece
Guatemala   Hungary   Italy   Japan   Poland   Portugal   Singapore
South Korea   Switzerland   Thailand   Turkey   Ukraine   Vietnam

Oxford is a registered trade mark of Oxford University Press in the UK and in certain other countries

This adaptation of The Garbage King © Oladipo Agboluaje 2013

Activity section © Oxford University Press 2013

The moral rights of the author have been asserted

Database right Oxford University Press (maker)

First published in 2013

British Library Cataloguing in Publication Data

Data available

ISBN 978 019 913802 9

10 9 8 7 6 5 4 3 2 1

MIX
Paper from
responsible sources
FSC FSC® C007785

Typeset in India by TNQ Books and Journals Pvt. Ltd.
Printed in Great Britain by Bell and Bain Ltd, Glasgow.

Acknowledgements
Extract from *The Garbage King* by Elizabeth Laird (Macmillan, 2003), reprinted by permission of Macmillan
Children's Books, London, UK.

The Publisher would like to thank Jenny Roberts for writing the Activity section.

Although we have made every effort to trace and contact all copyright holders before publication this has not been
possible in all cases. If notified, the publisher will rectify any errors or omissions at the earliest opportunity.

Cover image: © Jane Sweeney / Getty
About the author: Elizabeth Laird; p95: © John Van Hasselt / Corbis; p104: Natalia Sheinkin / Shutterstock
Artwork by Robin Lawrie

Contents

Rosamunde Hutt, the former associate director of the Unicorn Theatre, came to me with the idea of adapting Elizabeth Laird's *The Garbage King*. I hadn't come across Elizabeth's novel before. As I read it, I got drawn to the story of two boys from different backgrounds who develop an unlikely friendship in order to survive. The novel read like an adventure story with kidnap, chases, daring escapes and romance. But the story of Dani and Mamo's unlikely friendship continued to come through and with it the themes of sacrifice, finding oneself, determination to survive the worst the world can throw at you, and hope. I was also drawn to the plight of the street children of Addis Ababa. Elizabeth gives a vivid account of what it is to live on the streets, having to sift through rubbish to find things to sell, having to eat leftovers from the dustbins, and having to sleep with no roof over your head.

My first challenge (fear, to be honest) is that although I'm of African heritage I've never been to Ethiopia. Nigeria, where I spent a lot of my childhood, is very different from Ethiopia – different languages, different ways of dressing, different cultures. I could not take anything for granted. I had to gather and absorb as much information as I could about Addis Ababa to get an idea of the world in which *The Garbage King* is set.

At the time I was commissioned to adapt *The Garbage King* the Unicorn Theatre had an in-house ensemble of six very talented and committed actors. They came in from the start of the development process. They had read the book. We began with some workshops based on the themes of the novel. I then went off to write a number of drafts before we met for another workshop. In between the workshops, two of the actors had gone on a two-week holiday to Addis Ababa. (I told you they were committed. I did most of my research by scouring the Internet!) They came back with a treasure trove of videos and photographs of the capital city, which they presented to the creative team during the second workshop.

The play does not differ from the novel in any significant aspects. The core of the novel, Mamo and Dani's relationship, is the same. Fans of Liz's writing can expect to find most of the high points of the novel in the play. The real problem was what to leave out. Because I wanted to concentrate only on Mamo and Dani's story, I was going to leave out Tiggist. I soon realized how important she is as a character in her own right, as well as being part of Mamo's story, so she had to stay. There were many instances like this throughout the writing process.

The episodic structure was the only option for me to tell such an epic story with so many characters and so many locations. This structure also meant very fast scene and costume changes. We had only seven actors (the Unicorn recruited an additional actor to join the ensemble) which meant we had to juggle around scenes to take into consideration which actor was on stage playing one character but would be needed in the next scene immediately to play a different character. Certain scenes could not be moved or the story would not make sense. The actors had to be very fast at getting in and out of their costumes!

Oladipo Agboluaje

About the Author

 Elizabeth Laird was born in New Zealand of Scottish parents. She has lived in Ethiopia, Malaysia, Iraq, Lebanon and Austria. She now lives in Britain with her husband, David McDowall, who is also a writer. They divide their time between London and Edinburgh.

Elizabeth Laird has won many awards, including The Children's Book Award, and has been shortlisted five times for the Carnegie Medal. Some of her books are set in contemporary Britain, while others tackle modern issues in the Middle East and Africa. She has also written four historical novels. Her work has been translated into more than twenty languages.

For more information, visit her website at elizabethlaird. co.uk.

A Note on Staging

Our set was rubbish. Piles of rubbish! It was from the set that the actors 'found' their props. For instance, in the Unicorn production, Suri the puppy was an old hairdryer, with a hanging wire for its tail. Suri was controlled by different actors throughout the play depending on the scene's requirements. Merga's car and the bus with which Merga takes Mamo to the Farmer's village were made out of disused tyres and pieces of wood. The idea was that the sets were improvised, very much in keeping with how the street kids find uses for the things they scavenge from the rubbish heaps. The good thing about creating the sets in this way was that we didn't have to take sets off the stage and bring them on. The set changes were very quick. This allowed for scenes to bleed into each other. One piece of 'rubbish' in one scene became a prop or part of a set in another scene.

I would encourage a similar concept for any teacher or group wishing to stage *The Garbage King*. It is more about thinking what you can do with the objects you have rather than trying to find the actual objects you need.

For music we had a musician on stage who played traditional Ethiopian instruments. I'd say to any teacher or student, create your own soundscape – music, sound effects – using the props as drums, and if you've any other instruments at hand, that's fine too. A little research will uncover the rich musical heritage of Ethiopia that will help direct the musical style. We used music to mark places, such as hymns for when Getachew and Mamo are outside the church, as well as street sounds at the beginning of scenes when and where necessary.

We did have some sound effects such as the police siren and a splash as the Farmer's cow falls into the stream, but we kept them to a minimum.

COSTUME AND PROPS

ACT 1 SCENE 1: **The cemetery**

Two tombstones (the lighting is dim: we can barely make out Dani when Mamo runs into the cemetery to escape the Policeman)

Sounds: a crow squawking

Dani: smart short-sleeved shirt and jeans, a baseball cap, trainers, a travel bag, a stick (note that his clothes get dirtier as the play progresses)

Mamo: dirty shorts, a dirty vest, a dirty blanket, a bottle

Policeman: a torch

ACT 1 SCENE 2: **Mamo's home** (Mamo's house is set up while Scene 1 is still running)

Either a mat or a thin single-sized mattress, blanket, pillow, clothes, wooden stool, bucket

Tiggist: a wrapper, another bucket, a plastic bag with soap and a sponge inside, slippers/shoes, money

Merga: shirt, trousers, sandals

ACT 1 SCENE 3: **A motor park, Addis Ababa**

Sounds: car horns, bustle of street traders

Bus: can be represented by actors moving in tandem to the bus's movement or by two rows of chairs

Passengers: wearing a mix of traditional Ethiopian and western clothing

ACT 1 SCENE 4: **The farm**

Sticks and stones on the ground, a bush of poisonous leaves, two cattle sticks

Sounds: chickens, cows, a stream

Farmer: traditional clothes, cattle stick, coins

Farmer's wife: traditional clothes, bowl with chicken feed, half a cob of corn

Tesfaye: school uniform

Hailu: traditional clothes, cattle stick

Yohannes: traditional clothes, cattle stick, food for Mamo

ACT 1 SCENE 5: **Dani's house: the sitting room and Dani's room** (Dani's house is set up while Scene 4 is still running)

Sitting room:	A table, a chair, a standing lamp, a rug, Dani's notebook and exercise book, a pen or pencil, a bottle of water, a glass of water, tablets
Dani's room:	A pile of Dani's clothes, Dani's travel bag, a jar of money
Paulos:	dark suit, briefcase, document, pen, school report
Zeni:	suitcase for Ruth

ACT 1 SCENE 6: Dani's house
A mobile phone for Paulos

ACT 1 SCENE 7: The cemetery
Mamo's bottle filled with water
A ten birr note

ACT 1 SCENE 8: Mrs Faridah's backyard, Awassa
A clothes line with clothes hanging on it

Sounds:	church bells
Salma:	a necklace from Yacob
Yacob:	shirt, trousers, leather slippers

ACT 1 SCENE 9: A roadside, Addis Ababa

Getachew:	two plastic bags containing food containers

ACT 1 SCENE 10: The cemetery

Sounds:	dog whining
Mamo:	a ten birr note, plastic bag containing food containers, bread, his blanket
Dani:	his travel bag with a yellow shirt inside
Suri:	as a puppet

ACT 2 SCENE 1: The boys' patch at the rubbish heap
Rubbish, in particular odd shoes/footwear and an empty bottle, a blanket

Sounds:	the sounds of Suri throughout the scene
The gang:	all wear scruffy, dirty clothes
Karate:	his cough syrup

ACT 2 SCENE 2: A hospital, London
Hospital bed for Ruth

ACT 2 SCENE 3: **Outside the restaurant; at the rubbish heap**
Restaurant: Cook's pot with food scraps and a dustbin
Rubbish heap: Rubbish, in particular: a hat, a flask, a plastic bottle
Dani: his travel bag with all the items of clothing that the gang share,
                    a five birr note

ACT 2 SCENE 4: **Dani's house**
                    Paulos's mobile phone

ACT 2 SCENE 5: **Outside the restaurant; at the rubbish heap**
Restaurant: Cook's pot with food scraps and a dustbin, money
Policeman: a photograph of Dani
Rubbish heap: Bottles for Million and Buffalo
Buffalo: blankets
Shoes: his handkerchief
Getachew: a glorious chunk of meat

ACT 2 SCENE 6: **Mrs Faridah's backyard, Awassa**
Tiggist: bucket, clothes

ACT 2 SCENE 7: **The boys' patch at the rubbish heap**
Shoes: syringe on the scrapheap (we need not see the syringe – Shoes
                    reacts to being stabbed by the syringe)
Dani: notebook and plastic bag
Million: bag of bread rolls
Getachew: cigarette packet and lighter
Buffalo: stick to cane Getachew with

ACT 3 SCENE 1: **A hospital, London; a hospital, Addis Ababa**
Sounds: a bell to signal the end of visiting hours
                    Hospital bed for Ruth
                    Hospital bed for Karate, hospital pyjamas, chair
Shoes: bandage

ACT 3 SCENE 2: **A lake, Awassa**
Yacob: a small piece of paper

ACT 3 SCENE 3:   The boys' patch at the rubbish heap
                  A stretcher
Municipal workers: in overalls, pen and notebook for Worker 1

ACT 3 SCENE 4:   Outside Dani's house; at the rubbish heap
Sweet Seller: tray of sweets, a stool for her sweets, a stool for her to sit on, a cup
Dani: a pen
Paulos: black clothes
Guest: black clothes

ACT 3 SCENE 5:   The boys' patch at the rubbish heap
                  The boys' blankets, two bags of plastic containers with food, coins
Shoes: his handkerchief
Dani: pen and notebook

ACT 3 SCENE 6:   Dani's home: the sitting room
Ato Mesfin: pages of the story ripped from Dani's notebook
Paulos: his stick

ACT 3 SCENE 7:   The boys' patch at the rubbish heap
Mamo: coins

ACT 3 SCENE 8:   Mrs Faridah's shop, Addis Ababa
                  A stool, a table with boxes on it
Tiggist: the piece of paper with Yacob's number on it

ACT 3 SCENE 9:   Outside the restaurant; by the boys' patch at the rubbish heap
                  Merga's car, made up of a seat and two or four tyres
Shoes: a dirty linen as a bandage
Merga: he wears an expensive caftan, a wallet containing birr notes
Dani: a marker pen
Buffalo: a shopping bag
Mamo: a stick, Dani's notebook and pen
The boys: nails and spikes from the rubbish heap, tyres, celebratory drinks, crates to sit on

Character List

Mamo	A street kid, Dani's friend, age 12
Dani	A rich boy who has run away from home, age 12
Tiggist	Mamo's sister, age 19
Getachew	Street kid, Mamo's friend, age 13
Merga	Child kidnapper, age 30
Farmer	
Farmer's Wife	
Tesfaye	Farmer's son, age 13
Hailu	Cattle herder, age 12
Yohannes	Hailu's younger brother, cattle herder, age 10
Ruth	Dani's very ill mother
Meseret	Dani's baby sister
Zeni	Ruth's maid
Paulos	Dani's very strict father
Feisal	Paulos's strict old army sergeant
Yasmin	Mrs Faridah's baby
Salma	Tiggist's friend, Mrs Faridah's maid

Yacob	Salma's brother
Million	Leader of the street kids, age 16
Buffalo	Street kid, age 16
Shoes	Street kid, age 14
Karate	Street kid, very ill, age 9
Mikhail	Dani's uncle
Ato Mesfin	Dani's teacher
Mrs Faridah	Tiggist's boss
Feleke	
Policeman	
Bus Passengers 1, 2 and 3	
Bus Driver	
Sweet Seller	
Passers-by	
Nurse	
Cook	
Municipal Worker 1	
Municipal Worker 2	
Funeral Guest	

ACT 1

SCENE 1

Night. A cemetery. **Mamo,** *his dirty blanket tucked under his armpit, dashes in and hides behind a tombstone. A* **Policeman** *enters, flashing his torch around, looking for* **Mamo.** *He cannot find him.* **Mamo** *raises his head, smiling cheekily. Unseen by* **Mamo** *lays* **Dani,** *wearing a baseball cap, asleep behind another tombstone. He uses a travel bag for a pillow.* **Dani** *stirs. The* **Policeman** *hears* **Dani** *and spins round. He is afraid the noise might be from a ghost.* **Mamo** *ducks.* **Policeman** *walks cautiously towards* **Mamo.** **Mamo** *shuts his eyes tight, praying for the* **Policeman** *not to find him. The* **Policeman** *creeps up to the tombstone where* **Mamo** *is hiding. He is about to look behind the tombstone when a crow squawks! The* **Policeman,** *afraid, runs off.* **Mamo** *exhales with relief. He sings Bob Marley's* Survival.

Mamo   '… like Daniel out of the lion's den, black survivors, survivors, survivors …'

Dani springs up at the sound of **Mamo**'s *singing. They surprise each other. We see that as well as his baseball cap* **Dani** *is smartly dressed in a short-sleeved shirt and jeans. He wears the latest trainers. He is as plump as* **Mamo** *is skinny.*

Mamo   Ah!

Dani   Ah!

They run in opposite directions, afraid of each other.

Mamo   [Crosses himself] In the name of the saints, return to the dead!

Dani   Who are you?

Mamo   [Looks closer] Ha! I thought you were a ghost. Hi … [Takes a step forward]

Dani clutches his bag tighter.

I'm not a thief! I just want to bed down for the night.

Dani	Find somewhere else.
Mamo	Excuse me?
Dani	I was here first.
Mamo	I don't think so. *[Playfully acts like a zombie]*
Dani	Just go!

Mamo shakes his head as he walks back to his blanket. He unfurls it to reveal a bottle of water.

[Picks up a stick. Wields it uncertainly] Hey!

Mamo turns round. Dani readies himself to take a swing at Mamo. Mamo adopts a kung fu pose.

Mamo	Hiya! Bruce Lee, Jet Li, Jackie Chan!

Dani retreats. A crow squawks. Both react with fright. Dani drops his stick. Mamo cowers. They look sheepishly at each other.

[Moves his blanket away from Dani] I'll stay on this side, yeah?

Dani watches Mamo, wary. Mamo drinks water from his bottle. Dani watches him thirstily. Mamo offers Dani the bottle. Dani grabs it and glugs down the water.

Don't finish it!

Mamo snatches the bottle from an embarrassed Dani. Dani returns to his 'bed'.

The night gets cooler. Dani shivers, rubbing his arms, as Mamo covers himself with his large blanket. Mamo scrutinizes Dani, taking in his awkwardness.

Mamo	We can share my blanket. It's big enough for the two of us.

Dani glances at Mamo. He turns away, rubbing his shoulders vigorously.

I don't smell that bad … Suit yourself. *[Turns over to sleep]*

After a while Dani can no longer fight the cold. He sees that Mamo is still and creeps under the blanket so as not to wake up Mamo. He reacts to the smell by holding his nose before gently putting down his bag to use as a pillow.

[Without turning round] I'm Mamo, by the way.

Dani	*[Caught out. Sheepish]* My name's Dani.
Mamo	*[Turns round]* So what's a rich kid like you doing sleeping out in a cemetery?
Dani	*[Blusters]* I'm not rich.
Mamo	I've never seen a street kid dressed like you before.
Dani	I'm not a street kid. If you must know I ran away from home.
Mamo	You ran away? Why?
Dani	It's complicated.
Mamo	Try me.
Dani	My grades were poor.

Dani sees that Mamo thinks he is joking.

My father wanted to send me away to live with his old army sergeant.

Mamo cannot believe his ears.

ACT 1   SCENE 1

16

	You don't know Feisal. He lived with us until Mum sacked him for beating me … *[Sees **Mamo** is unimpressed]* You don't get it.
Mamo	You're right. It is complicated.
	Uneasy silence.
Dani	Where do you sleep, apart from here?
Mamo	Hey, I'm not a street kid. I lived in a room with my sister. I went back there, she was gone and someone else was living there.
Dani	I was only asking—
	A police car passes, siren wailing. **Dani** *and* **Mamo** *frantically pull the blanket over their heads.*
	[Under the blanket] What are you hiding for?
Mamo	*[Under the blanket]* What are you hiding for?
Dani	*[Under the blanket]* The police are looking for me.
Mamo	*[Throws off the blanket]* They're looking for me too!
Dani	Sh!
	They pull the blanket back over their heads and stay still. Slowly their heads appear.
	Upstage from the cemetery, actors set up **Mamo's** *house ready for Act 1 Scene 2.*
Dani	My father would have told them I'm missing. Why are they looking for you?
Mamo	You really want to know?
Dani	Yes.
Mamo	I was kidnapped!
Dani	Don't lie!
	Mamo *drags the blanket off* **Dani** *and rolls with it onto his bed at home as he acts out his story.* **Dani** *stays in the cemetery scene, listening eagerly. He rubs his shoulders to keep warm.*

Mamo's home: a shack furnished with a bed and a wooden stool, next to which is an old plastic bucket. Mamo's few clothes are scattered all over the room. Outside, Tiggist, Mamo's sister, dressed in a wrapper, holding another plastic bucket and a plastic bag containing her sponge and soap, with Getachew, Mamo's friend. He is as skinny as Mamo. He has a cheeky grin on his face. Tiggist does not like him.

Tiggist   *[Sternly]* I will tell him you came by. Goodbye Getachew.

Getachew stays where he is.

What are you still hanging about for?

Getachew is not moving. Tiggist reaches for her slipper. Getachew runs away.

Truant. *[Puts her slipper back on her foot]*

Tiggist enters the shack to find Mamo sleeping. She looks at Mamo's clothes in dismay.

Can't you look after yourself for once? *[Hastily picks up Mamo's clothes]* I told you to be up by the time I finish from the bathroom, but oh no …

Mamo hasn't stirred. Tiggist pulls the blanket off him.

Tiggist   Up! You're making me late for work!

Mamo   *[Stays in bed]* Mm …

Tiggist   *[Hits him with the blanket]* I said get up!

Mamo yawns and stretches. At last he gets up and makes the bed.

Mamo   Did you speak to Mrs Hannah?

Tiggist   *[Gets dressed]* She says she cannot lend us any money.

Mamo   It's almost the end of the month. How do we pay the rent?

Tiggist   I don't know, Mamo.

18

Mamo	Promise me you won't do for money what mother did.
Tiggist	At this rate, I'll have to.
Mamo	Tiggist!
Tiggist	Go and have your bath.
Mamo	I'd rather be homeless than see you turn into mother.
Tiggist	Someone else will get to the bathroom!
Mamo	I mean it.
Tiggist	OK, Mamo.

Tiggist turns to **Mamo**. *She sees he is serious.*

OK. Now go. Mrs Hannah needs her bucket.

Mamo *heads for the bucket in the room.*

I told you to throw that away.

Mamo	This is a new one.

Mamo *hands her the bucket. She looks at him quizzically.*

I found it behind the carpenter's shed. We won't need to borrow Mrs Hannah's bucket anymore.

Tiggist hands back the bucket. *She is impressed.*

Tiggist	You're so good at finding things. [*Sighs, more to herself*] I wish you could find us the money for the rent.
Mamo	What about breakfast?
Tiggist	I'll give you money for some bread. And when you go, make sure it's to the baker's and back. You hear me? … Mamo!
Mamo	*Yes.* Uh!

Mamo *heads for the door.*

Tiggist	Mamo … I am going to ask Mrs Faridah if we can sleep in her shop.

Mamo	She won't let me stay with you. She'll think I'll steal the sweets from her shop at night.
Tiggist	Mrs Faridah isn't like that.
Mamo	She's a shop owner. They're all like that.
Tiggist	When you hang around street corners all day with thieves like Getachew what do you expect her to think? Anyway I'm sure she won't mind. We'll be her security. I'll be near her house. I can help her look after little Yasmin. She might give you a job as her houseboy.
Mamo	What about that shoeshine kit you promised me?
Tiggist	I can't afford it right now. Being a houseboy is safer. You'll be fed and have a roof over your head. Mrs Faridah might even send you to school.
Mamo	I'll bring Getachew round. He'll tell you how his old mistress always beat him and starved him.
Tiggist	And living on the street is better? You'd rather beg and steal than do an honest job?
Mamo	Shining shoes is honest work.
Tiggist	How will you defend yourself when bigger boys drive you off your patch and steal your kit?
Mamo	I can defend myself.
Tiggist	With your TV kung fu?
Mamo	I like it here. Why do we have to leave?
Tiggist	Mamo, we have no choice. Even if you get work we'll never raise the fifty birr for the rent by the end of the month.
Mamo	Fifty birr!
Tiggist	We'll stay in the shop just until I can save money and we can get a cheaper room of our own. I can buy gifts for little Yasmin.
Mamo	Oh, no money for my kit but you have money to buy Yasmin presents. She's not your baby.

Tiggist	You are not a baby.
Mamo	I'm still your brother.
Tiggist	I do the best I can, Mamo. Let someone look after me for once. Here. *[Gives him money]* For the bread. Return Mrs Hannah's bucket to her. Don't forget to lock the door when you go out.

Mamo flops onto the bed and covers his ears with the pillow.

Be here by the time I'm back or I'll go and live with Mrs Faridah without you and you can live on the streets with your friends. You hear? Mamo! Huh! *[Exits in a huff]*

Mamo	I'm not going! I'm staying here!

Merga, shifty-looking, barges in without knocking. He is in a worn-out shirt and trousers.

Merga	Where is my …!

Mamo is startled.

Oh, um, where's your mother?

Mamo	Who are you?
Merga	You don't remember me, Mm … *[Pretends trying to remember his name]*
Mamo	Mamo.
Merga	Mamo! It's me, Uncle Merga, your mother's brother.
Mamo	Mother never told me I had an uncle.
Merga	Where is she?
Mamo	She died last week.
Merga	She owes me money!
Mamo	You're not one of her customers, are you?
Merga	I will pull your ear! I said I'm your uncle. *[Searches around]* Did she leave me anything?
Mamo	Like what?

Merga	Just tell me where her valuables are.
Mamo	Huh?
Merga	You mean this is all there is? *[Scrutinizes **Mamo**]* How old are you?
Mamo	Thirteen.
Merga	Uh-huh.
Mamo	I'm an ambitious twelve.
Merga	You work?
Mamo	I'm about to. I want to shine shoes.
Merga	I can get you a real job.
Mamo	You can? Will I be able to pay my rent? It's fifty birr.
Merga	No problem.
Mamo	It's *fifty* birr.
Merga	I heard you the first time, kid.
Mamo	*[To **Dani**]* A job. A real job. *[To **Merga**]* When do I start?
Merga	That's the spirit. *[Ushers **Mamo** to the door]*
Mamo	Right now? I haven't had my bath.
Merga	You want the job or not?

*Mamo follows **Merga**, then **Mamo** runs back to the shack.*

What now?

Mamo	*[Locks the door]* Have to lock up or Tiggist will tell me off.

*As **Mamo** locks the door, actors remove the set of the room and use the props to set up a bus. The actors play the **Passengers** and the **Driver**. Gently the noise of a busy motor park rises.*

Merga	Hurry up, then. *[Walks off]*

*Light on **Dani** in the graveyard.*

Dani	You went away with a stranger?

| Mamo | [To Dani] I had no choice. Tiggist always nagged me to look after myself. She was going to be shocked. We wouldn't have to live in Mrs Faridah's shop. And it would be thanks to me … |

*Light goes down on **Dani** in the graveyard. He waits eagerly for **Mamo** to tell the next part of the story.*

***Merga** grabs **Mamo** by the arm and leads him to sit in the bus.*

• •

SCENE 3

***Mamo** hears the **Bus Driver** call out a countryside destination. He grows suspicious.*

Mamo	This bus is headed for the country.
Merga	Be quiet.
Mamo	You said this job is here in Addis.

Merga ignores him.

How far is this place we're going to?

| Merga | Kid … |
| Mamo | My name is Mamo. |

Merga	You wanted a job, I've got you one. Now be quiet.
Mamo	How come my mother never mentioned you?
Merga	Ask her yourself.
Mamo	I told you, she's dead.

Merga ignores him.

[Stands up] You're not my uncle.

Merga	*[Sits **Mamo** down]* Sit down.
Mamo	You are one of her customers!

Mamo stands up. Merga forces him to sit down again.

[Jumps up, cries] Help! He's kidnapping me! Help!

Merga	I'm getting my lazy nephew a job. He doesn't want to work.
Passenger 1	In these hard times? And this is how you repay your uncle?
Passenger 2	Children nowadays. Lazy ingrates.

Passengers murmur in agreement.

Passenger 1	My nephew wants his mum to serve him breakfast in bed and bathe him, like he's some prince.
Passenger 2	Is that why you didn't bath this morning, to come and kill us with your foul odour? Your uncle—
Mamo	He's not my uncle!
Merga	I was your Uncle Merga when I bought you sweets.
Passenger 1	It's the same with my nephew.
Mamo	He is not my uncle! I don't know him!
Passenger 3	Mister! If he doesn't want to work send him back home.
Mamo	Yes, send me home.
Passenger 3	You can't force him to work. He can do something else …
Mamo	Thank you, sir!

Passenger 3	… Like roam the streets with your gang and rob an honest man like me …
Mamo	No, sir, I'm not in a gang.
Passenger 3	… Because it's every day that I get a bonus from work to 'donate' it to you rats! *[To Merga]* Mister, if you don't know how to use your shoe on his sooty behind I will show you.
Mamo	I'm telling the truth—
Passenger 3	Quiet! I don't want to hear your voice for the rest of this journey.
Mamo	But—
Passenger 3	Quiet!
	Passengers murmur in solidarity with Merga. Mamo is subdued.
Merga	Thank you sir, thank you madam. *[Holds Mamo by the neck, choking him]* Careful, kid. *Careful.*
Mamo	Please let me go. Please …
	The bus moves. The sounds of the countryside are heard as the actors remove the set of the bus and set up a village backyard. Actors play the cows using props for horns.
Mamo	*[To Dani]* On we went, for miles and miles away from Addis. Where was this man taking me?
	Dani is captivated by Mamo's story.

● ●

SCENE 4

The **Farmer**'s house. On the ground are two cattle sticks. **Farmer**, strict looking, holding a cattle stick of his own, counts money. The **Farmer's Wife**, unsmiling, feeds the chickens. **Tesfaye**, their son, in his school uniform, is tending to some cows. He glares at the frightened **Mamo**. **Farmer** pays **Merga**. **Merga** counts the money.

Merga	Next time I won't accept this pittance. *[Reluctantly pockets the money]*
Farmer	Next time bring me a 13-year-old like I asked for.
Farmer's Wife	He's skinnier than a cattle stick. He'd better not be the hungry type.
Merga	He's not my problem now. *[Walks off]*
Mamo	You can't leave me here. Please take me back. *[Clings to **Merga**]*
Merga	Let go, kid.

*Farmer pulls him off **Merga**. **Mamo** struggles. **Merga** exits.*

Mamo	Uncle Merga! Please!

*Farmer hits him hard with his stick. **Mamo** falls to the ground.*

Aw! My mother!

Farmer	Quiet! You do your work, there will be no problem. If you don't, I will beat you until you bleed. Get up! *[Hits **Mamo** with his stick]*

Mamo jumps up, petrified.

Tesfaye!

Tesfaye	Yes, Father!
Farmer	Show the boy what to do.
Tesfaye	I'll be late for school.
Farmer	Do as I say!

*Tesfaye picks up one of the cattle sticks. **Farmer** pats the black cow's stomach. It is pregnant.*

Farmer	Just a few weeks until you calve, eh?
Tesfaye	Father! I got ten marks out of ten in my Geography homework …

*Farmer ignores **Tesfaye** and exits.*

*Farmer's Wife throws half a cob of corn at **Mamo**'s feet.*

Farmer's Wife   That's your meal for the day. Don't ask for more.

*Mamo greedily eats the corn. The **Farmer's Wife** looks at him with disdain.*

What do you say?

*Mamo continues eating. The **Farmer's Wife** huffs. She exits.*

Tesfaye   Pick up that stick.

*Mamo continues eating. **Tesfaye** knocks the corn out of **Mamo**'s hands. **Mamo** tries to retrieve the corn. **Tesfaye** kicks the corn to the chickens.*

Listen, you filthy city rat. Make me late for school and my father will thrash you. Try to escape and he'll feed your carcass to the hyenas like he did to the last rat who worked for him. Now pick up the stick!

Mamo picks up the cattle stick.

To make them move you swing your stick like this.

*Tesfaye swings his stick. **Mamo** copies his gestures clumsily.*

Are you blind? Like this.

27

*Tesfaye repeats the gesture. **Mamo** copies him. He gets better at it. They herd the cattle away. **Tesfaye** steers a cow away from a plant. He holds up a leaf from the plant to show to **Mamo**.*

Tesfaye	If you see them go near this plant, drive them away. The leaves are poisonous. If anything happens to these cows you are dead. You hear me?

*Mamo nods. They continue to herd the cattle until they get to a stream. **Tesfaye** exits.*

Mamo looks around, hungry. He plucks unripe fruit from a tree to eat. The cows low. He drives them to the stream.

Mamo	[To **Dani**] For two weeks I worked like a dog under the harsh sun. There were times I was so hungry I could hear my name being carried by the wind.

*In the background **Tiggist**, at their home in Addis Ababa, enters, smiling.*

Tiggist	Mamo! Mamo?

*Tiggist looks around for **Mamo**. Her disbelief turns to anger. She exits.*

Mamo	[To **Dani**] I wondered if Tiggist knew where I was. I prayed she would come and save me.

*Hailu and his younger brother **Yohannes** enter. They are friendly and eager. **Hailu** is Mamo's age. **Yohannes** is 10. **Yohannes** gives **Mamo** some food. **Mamo** drops the unripe fruit and gratefully wolfs the food down.*

Mamo	It was in my third week there that I met:
Yohannes	Yohannes.
Hailu	I'm Hailu.
Mamo	Mamo. Thanks for the food.
Yohannes	We were wondering how long it would be before we got to meet you.

Hailu	Your master doesn't like us befriending his workers. We saw the last boy only once. We never got to know his name.
Mamo	Is it true that Tesfaye's dad fed him to the hyenas?
Yohannes	Yes.
Hailu	For trying to escape.
	*Mamo is scared. **Yohannes** and **Hailu** burst out laughing. **Mamo** realizes they were pulling his leg. He smiles.*
Mamo	Are they always this horrible?
Yohannes	Always.
Hailu	Not always.
Yohannes	He's harsh with everyone. He's a nasty man.
	The black cow wanders close to the stream.
Hailu	Go check on the cows!
Yohannes	It's your turn.
Mamo	I don't care whether—
Hailu	Oh! *[Points to the black cow]*
Mamo	Ah!
	Mamo runs to the black cow and herds it away from the stream.
Hailu	Don't let them get too close to the stream, especially that one. She's their prize breeder. She will calve in a few days' time.
Yohannes	No. She will calve in two weeks.
Hailu	What do you know about cows?
Yohannes	More than you do.
	Hailu clouts Yohannes.
Mamo	You two sound just like me and my sister.
	*They see the glint of sadness in **Mamo**'s eyes. They feel sympathy for **Mamo**.*

29

Hailu	If your uncle brought you, he'll have told your sister you're here. She'll come and get you.
Mamo	Merga is not my uncle.
Yohannes	You could write to her.
Mamo	I can't write.
Yohannes	Tesfaye knows how to write.
Hailu	Don't be stupid. He's not going to ask Tesfaye.
Mamo	How do I get back to Addis?
Hailu	We don't know how.
Mamo	You must know!
Hailu	We've never left the village.
Yohannes	If you work a few more months for your master, he might release you.
Mamo	He'll have beaten me to death. Last week he slapped me for dozing off – at night!
Hailu	You are too soft.
Mamo	Me, soft? You wouldn't last a second in Addis.
Yohannes	Is Addis really as dangerous as they say?
Mamo	*[Does kung fu moves]* Haya! I eat danger morning, noon and night.
Yohannes	Where did you learn kung fu?
Mamo	From the three Shaolin masters: Sony, Toshiba and Panasonic.
Hailu	You've seen a television?
Mamo	*[Dismissive]* Puh!
Hailu	Some of the music they play on the radio. I don't understand it.
Mamo	It's in English. I can teach you.

Mamo sings Survival. *Hailu* and *Yohannes* *try to sing with him.*

Tesfaye enters, still in his school uniform.

Tesfaye	What are you doing with the city rat? You want to catch his disease?
Mamo	My name is Mamo.
Tesfaye	Getting bold now, are you?
Mamo	Don't call me city rat.
Tesfaye	Or what?
Mamo	Call me that again and you'll find out.
Yohannes	He knows kung fu.
Tesfaye	City rat.

*Mamo drops his stick and approaches **Tesfaye**. **Tesfaye** picks up a stone and throws it at **Mamo**. **Mamo** ducks. The stone hits the black cow, causing it to lurch forward in panic. Splash! The black cow falls into the stream.*

The cow!

The boys rush into the stream. They pull the black cow out. They are too late. The cow is dead.

My father is going to kill you!

Mamo	You threw the stone!

Farmer enters.

Farmer	I could hear you all the … *[Sees the cow]* Father in heaven. Is that my cow? *[Rushes into the stream]* My prize cow! You've drowned her!

*Enraged **Farmer** grabs **Mamo**. **Hailu** and **Yohannes** run away.*

Mamo	Please, sir! It was Tesfaye! It was Tesfaye! Yohannes! Hailu, tell him! Tell him!

*Farmer thrashes **Mamo**.*

My mother! My mother, save me!

Mamo lies prone. Farmer storms off. Tesfaye looks at Mamo, frightened. He runs off. Mamo staggers to the poisonous plant. Tearfully, he rips off some leaves and stuffs them in his mouth.

Dani	You tried to kill yourself?
Mamo	I made up that part.
Dani	Oh. It sounded very real to me.
Mamo	That's storytelling, my friend. Didn't they teach you that in your school?
Dani	Yes. My Amharic* and History teacher *Ato*** Mesfin says I'm his best student.
Mamo	Well, then.
Dani	This farmer sounds just like Feisal.
Mamo	I thought rich parents spoilt their kids.
Dani	My dad blames me for everything, even for my mother's illness. If not for her he'd have sent me away sooner.
Mamo	Your mother's ill? And you left her?

The actors clear away the set. They set up the sitting room of Dani's house with a rug, a standing lamp and a chair. On the rug they put down Dani's notebook and exercise book, one on top of the other and a pen. Further upstage they create Dani's room with just Dani's travel bag, a small money jar and a heap of Dani's clothes.

Dani	She's not at home.
Mamo	She ran away too?
Dani	No.
Mamo	Then tell me. Oh, I get it. It's complicated.

Dani looks away, insecure.

Mamo	I'll give you the rest of my water. *[Offers Dani his bottle of water]*

---

* 'Amharic' is the language spoken in Ethiopia.
** 'Ato' can be translated as 'Mister'.

Dani gratefully takes the water. He finishes it as he walks into the set. Mamo sits on the ground by the edge of the rug. He touches the rug. It is the smoothest, softest thing he has ever touched. He marvels at the wealth of Dani's house as he listens to Dani's story.

● ●

SCENE 5

Dani's home. The sitting room.
Ruth, Dani's mother, holds Dani's baby sister, Meseret, in one arm. She holds up a glass with her other hand, and Dani enters, finishing the water.

Ruth	I said don't finish it, Dani.
Dani	*[Jokily]* Sorry!

Dani puts down the empty bottle and writes in his notebook under which is his arithmetic exercise book. Ruth coughs as Zeni, the maid, enters with tablets. She takes Meseret off Ruth. Ruth takes the tablets from Zeni. She hands Zeni the glass. Zeni exits.

[Flourishes with a final full stop] I've finished my story!

Ruth	Let's hear it.
Dani	There were two brothers who lived in a house all on their own because their parents went out one day and never came back.

Zeni returns with the glass filled with water. Ruth swallows her tablets with the water. Zeni exits.

The brothers were hungry because there was no one to cook for them. Then one day the older brother said, we have to go out to find food or else we will starve.

Ruth	Why didn't they go out before?
Dani	Um. *[Thinks]* Ah! Because their parents never let them leave the house. They had never ever gone outside. But now …

Paulos, Dani's father, enters. He wears a dark suit and has a briefcase. He looks very severe. Dani hides his story notebook under his arithmetic exercise book. He starts working on a problem in the

33

*arithmetic exercise book. He strains to find an answer. **Paulos** snaps his fingers. **Dani** hands **Paulos** the arithmetic exercise book.*

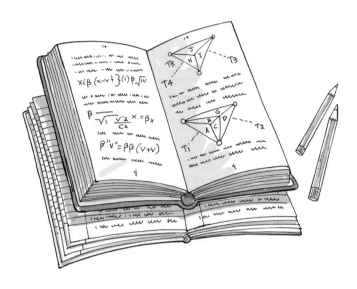

Paulos	It's a wonder your teachers can read your homework.
Ruth	Encourage him for once, Paulos.
Paulos	*[Finally reads **Dani**'s handwriting]* Ah! Twelve times nine, Dani!
	***Dani** counts with his fingers.*
	I will cut off your fingers!
Ruth	Don't shout at him.
Paulos	Dani. What is twelve times nine?
Ruth	Paulos!
Paulos	*[Brings out a document from his suit pocket]* You're lucky your mother is here. I would have thrashed you until you gave me the answer. *[Gives **Ruth** the document]*
Ruth	*[Reads the document. Her face drops]* Finish your homework in your room.
Paulos	By the time you come out you'd better have the correct answer. Stupid boy.

Dani goes to his room. He listens by the door.

Ruth	I thought I didn't need to go.
Paulos	Dr Ahmed says there is nothing more the hospitals here can do for you.
Ruth	How long will I have to be in London?

Dani is shaken.

Paulos	For as long as it takes to get you better.
Ruth	That could be weeks or months even. To be away from you for that long …
Paulos	It's the only option, Ruth. *[Offers her a pen]* Now sign it so I can fax it back to the hospital.
Ruth	*[Takes the pen]* Promise me you won't be rash with Dani while I'm gone.
Dani	*[Prays]* Don't sign it. Please don't sign it.
Paulos	He is useless at everything useful. You saw his last school report.
Ruth	I asked you to get him a lesson teacher.
Paulos	I got him a lesson teacher before. What good did it do? I am dreading his next exam results already. If he fails again I'll—
Ruth	Has your beating him helped him improve?
Paulos	It's not just his education. He is gutless. I'm not surprised none of his schoolmates comes round. Who wants to be friends with a loser?
Ruth	My son is not a loser!

Ruth stands. She is racked by a cough. Paulos eases her back down.

Promise.

Paulos	I promise I'll try. What? I've never lied to you. Do you want me to start now?

*Ruth signs the paper. She hands it back to **Paulos**. **Dani** is crestfallen.*

Ruth	Dani!
Dani	Yes, Mum.

***Dani** returns, miserable.*

Ruth	*[Coughs]* I have to go to London for treatment. It's the only way I'll get better. You want me to get better, don't you?
Paulos	Don't ask him. He'll give the wrong answer.
Ruth	Paulos! *[To **Dani**]* Once I get better I'll come straight home, I promise. While I'm gone you must look after your baby sister. And you must get better grades in your coming exams.
Dani	How long will you be away?
Ruth	I don't know, Dani. Will you do as I ask?
Dani	I will.
Ruth	Say it.
Dani	I will look after Meseret. I will pass my exams.
Ruth	That's my hero. Now, what do you want me to buy for you from London?

***Zeni** brings **Ruth**'s suitcase. **Ruth** waves goodbye to **Dani**. She exits with **Paulos**.*

Mamo	Your mother has gone to London?
Dani	Yes.
Mamo	In a plane?
Dani	Yes.
Mamo	Have you flown in one?
Dani	Twice, when we went on holiday to South Africa and when we went to Canada for my uncle's wedding.
Mamo	To where?

Dani	They are countries. Far away.
Mamo	Wow. And you weren't afraid you would crash?
Dani	No.
Mamo	*[Shivers at the thought of flying]* I'd close my eyes for the whole of the journey.

Paulos enters scowling, with Dani's school report.

Dani	When I close my eyes I imagine I can fly like Superman—
Paulos	Dani!
Dani	Yes, Father!
Paulos	See? Your report is dripping red ink! Arithmetic: fail. Geography: fail! Even PE! Dani! You can't move your legs?
Dani	I passed Amharic and History.
Paulos	Do you think I built my house with Amharic and History? Your Principal says you spend all day in class daydreaming. Thank God your mother is not here to see this. It would kill her. So, Dani, tell me, what do we do about this?
Dani	I will try harder, Father, I promise.
Paulos	No. You will not try harder because you cannot, not in this environment. You have everything too easy. When I was in the army, what do you think I learned?
Dani	To kill people.
Paulos	Yes. No! I learned self-discipline. That is what you need. Otherwise you'll end up a street child, begging and stealing because I certainly will not be supporting you. You want to become a street child?
Dani	No, Father.
Paulos	Good. I am sending you to live with Feisal.
Dani	Father!

Paulos	You will stay with him for one year. He will turn you into a man.
Dani	For one year! But what about my school?
Paulos	I've withdrawn you from your school.
Dani	Father, please give me one more chance.
Paulos	Get your stuff packed and ready. He is coming for you this evening.
Dani	This evening!
Paulos	This is for your own good, Dani. In the future you will thank me for this.

Paulos exits.

Dani goes to his room. Miserable, he picks up his bag and starts packing.

| Dani | *[To Mamo]* Feisal. He'd always say he couldn't believe I was my father's son. Once I kicked a ball into his garden. He beat me so hard I fainted. |
| Paulos | *[Off]* Are you packing or playing? |

Dani jumps up and finishes packing. He is crestfallen.

If Father wants me out of the way I'll go, but not to Feisal.

Dani empties his money jar into his pocket. He creeps out of the house. He runs off.

Paulos enters with Feisal, a strict sergeant major type. Mamo, at the sight of Feisal, runs back to the cemetery.

| Paulos | He's even more useless than when you were living with us … Dani? *[Goes into Dani's room]* He was here a minute ago… Dani! |

Dani escapes into the street. Sweet Seller, a kindly woman, sees him.

| Sweet Seller | Dani! I have your favourite sweets. |

Dani	Not today, thank you. *[Runs off]*
Sweet Seller	Are you unwell? Ah, you are missing your mother, poor child.

*Dani runs away into the cemetery and sits back down next to **Mamo**.*

Mamo	That's it?
Dani	Yes. You know, our stories sound the same.
Mamo	I was taken against my will.
Dani	I didn't want to go to Feisal.
Mamo	But in a year's time you'd be back in your big house. You left your sister.
Dani	Our maid will look after her. You left your sister too.
Mamo	She's older than me! And she left me.
Dani	But you said you left—
Mamo	You know what? Forget it. *[Tries to take a drink. The bottle is empty. He throws it down angrily and covers himself to go to sleep]*

*Dani looks at **Mamo**. He turns over.*

● ●

SCENE 6

*Dani's house. **Paulos** on his mobile phone. He paces up and down.*

Paulos	Dawit. Fine. Yes, she arrived safely, thank God. Please, did Gabriel see Dani today? No. You know how these boys are. Thanks. I will. Bye. *[Hangs up and dials a number]* Hello, Inspector! How are you? It's Dani. He's missing. He can't have gone far. No. I'll bring my own cane. By the time I finish with him he will never embarrass me again.

SCENE 7

*The cemetery. The next day. Early morning. **Dani** wakes. He turns to find **Mamo** is gone. **Dani** checks his bag. Nothing is missing. He sighs with relief. He realizes how hungry he is. **Mamo** enters with his bottle filled with water.*

Dani	I thought you'd gone.
Mamo	I went to get water.
Dani	What about food?
Mamo	I'm going into town to beg.
Dani	Could you bring some food back for me?
Mamo	I'm not your houseboy.
Dani	I can't go out because—
Mamo	Because the police are looking for you. Because they're not looking for me. You're not hungry.

Mamo makes to leave.

Dani	I have money! You could buy us food. You won't need to go far so you won't be seen. *[Gives **Mamo** a note]*

*Mamo reluctantly takes the money from **Dani**. He realizes how much it is.*

Mamo	This is ten birr! This should get us a full meal. *[Gives **Dani** the water]* There's a canteen nearby. I'll be back soon.

*Mamo runs off, singing a song. The song continues into the next scene to be picked up by **Tiggist**.*

Dani	*[Exhales with relief, then:]* What was I thinking? He's not coming back.

SCENE 8

*Church bells. Awassa, a town outside of Addis Ababa. In the backyard of Mrs Faridah's house, **Tiggist** sings the same song* as **Mamo** *as she fans the sleeping baby* **Yasmin**. *Nearby,* **Salma**, *a playful young girl, with her awkward brother* **Yacob**. **Tiggist** *stops singing and spies on them – she fancies* **Yacob**. **Yacob** *puts a necklace around* **Salma***'s neck.* **Salma** *hugs him.* **Yacob** *exits.* **Salma** *shows off the necklace to* **Tiggist**.

Salma	What do you think?
Tiggist	It's lovely. When next is Yacob going to Addis? I need to get in touch with Mamo.
Salma	Not for a while. So your neighbour hasn't seen him?
Tiggist	She says not since I came to Awassa.
Salma	He's having the time of his life without you being there to boss him around.
Tiggist	I told him I'd go by myself if I didn't find him at home.
Salma	There you go! He made his choice.
Tiggist	But he didn't know I'd leave Addis with Mrs Faridah.
Salma	A friend of mine is going to Addis. I'll ask him to drop by your house. Now stop worrying, OK?
	Salma exits. **Yasmin** *stirs.*
Tiggist	I'll sing you a song I used to sing to Mamo while he slept so that he could have sweet dreams. Maybe Mamo might hear us and it will lead him here to Awassa. *[Sings a lullaby]*

• •

SCENE 9

Addis Ababa. Roadside, by a church. **Mamo** *is with* **Getachew**. **Getachew** *has a bag of food. He is begging for more food from passers-by.*

41

Getachew	*[To a passing **Man**]* For the sake of Christ, sir, another for my poor mother.
Mamo	. . . So that's it man.
Getachew	No wonder I couldn't find you. I thought you'd gone with Tiggist. *[To a passing **Woman**]* For the sake of Gabriel, another . . .
Mamo	What was the name of the village she went to?
Getachew	I don't know. The man looking after Mrs Faridah's shop wouldn't tell me.
Mamo	She said she'd leave without me if I didn't come back. I didn't think she meant it.
Getachew	Maybe she didn't mean to.
Mamo	Then she'd have told someone where she was so I could find her. She left me.
Getachew	*[To a passing **Woman**]* For the love of God, please some food …
Mamo	Where have you been, anyway? I looked for you at your uncle's house.

Getachew	Ah. I've been in prison.
Mamo	What?
Getachew	Remember Feleke? He nicked some stuff off a street stall and pinned it on me. Anyway, when I got out my uncle told me to clear off. Not that I cared. He was using me as his houseboy. So I'm on the streets. *[To a passing **Woman**]* For the sake of Christ …

Woman gives him a bag of food.

Thank you, madam, God bless you. *[Gives the bag of food to Mamo]* Here.

Mamo	Oh, thanks, man.
Getachew	I've got to take this back to my *joviro**.
Mamo	Your what?
Getachew	My gangmaster.
Mamo	You're in a gang?
Getachew	Yeah. He has all these rules. We have to share everything we gather. If you've nowhere to stay I can get you in.
Mamo	Where do you guys crash?
Getachew	On the other side of town in this unfinished building. We call it 'the bridge'. It's very warm at night.
Mamo	Man, I've got to take this food back.
Getachew	Oh, you're in a gang already?
Mamo	Nah. I'm hanging with this rich kid. We spent the night in a cemetery.
Getachew	You're serious?
Mamo	Yeah.
Getachew	When he realizes you're not coming back, he'll go home … *[Walks off, expecting **Mamo** to follow him. He turns round to see*

---

* 'Joviro' can be translated as 'gangmaster'.

Mamo hasn't moved] What? You spend one night together – in a cemetery – and you're best friends? Come. *[Pulls Mamo by the arm]*

Mamo   Stop! *[Pulls away from Getachew]* I can walk by myself.

They exit together.

• •

SCENE 10

The cemetery. Dani, morose. He hears a whining noise. He heads in the direction of the noise. He sees Suri, a scraggy, lean and hungry puppy. She is full of cheeky mischief.

Dani   Oh, look at you. What's wrong, little girl? What's wrong? *[Picks up Suri]* Are you hungry? So am I. I've got some water. *[Gives Suri water]* You're the only friend I have in the world now.

Mamo enters with a bag of food. Suri runs to him.

Dani   Mamo!

Mamo   You thought I'd run away with your money? *[Hands Dani the ten birr note]*

Dani   *[Sheepish as he takes the money]* How did you pay for the food?

Mamo   My friend gave it to me. *[Hands Dani the bag of food]* Hello you. How are you? *[Pats Suri]* Where did you find her?

Dani hastily takes out the food and wolfs it down.

Dani   *[Mouth full]* She was lying down in the back there. She looks unwell.

Mamo   The food is for the two of us.

Dani stops eating. Mamo spreads out his blanket and lays out the food. Dani grabs at the bread. Mamo glares at him. Dani puts the bread back.

Mamo   *[Prays]* Father, for what we are about to receive we give you thanks. Amen.

Dani   Amen.

44

*Dani eats hungrily. He catches himself and slows down. **Mamo** feeds the dog injera*.*

Mamo	Here you go. You like that, don't you, Suri?
Dani	Suri?
Mamo	Oh, you've already given her a name.
Dani	No. Suri's fine.

*They finish the water. **Dani** takes the bottle and gets up.*

Mamo	I'm meeting my friend who got us the food. He says he'll get me into his gang.
Dani	What about me?

Mamo shrugs.

Can I come with you?

Mamo	No.
Dani	But I have nowhere else to go.
Mamo	Yes you do, Dani.
Dani	I just need somewhere to hide. I'll do whatever you ask me to.
Mamo	Even if I wanted to bring you along they won't take you. You'll stick out. *[Makes to leave]* Keep the bottle.
Dani	Wait!

Dani opens his bag and brings out a yellow shirt.

Mamo	*[Peeks at what else is inside **Dani**'s bag]* Dani …
Dani	It's for getting us the food. It's my favourite shirt. Mum bought it for me when we went to Canada.

*Mamo takes the shirt. He tries it on. He loves it. A thought comes to his head. He realizes he cannot take **Dani**'s shirt … He takes it off.*

---

* 'Injera' is a traditional Ethiopian bread.

Dani	Don't you like it? I have another one. *[Rummages through his bag]*
Mamo	*[Hands the shirt back to **Dani**]* The police will think I stole it.
Dani	Tell them I gave it to you.
	Mamo laughs.
	Tell your friends I've got money. I'll pay my way.
Mamo	And when the money runs out?
	Dani has no answer. Mamo puts the shirt in Dani's hand.
	Go home, Dani.
	Mamo leaves. Dani is crestfallen.
Dani	*[To Suri]* At least you haven't deserted me.
	Suri sniff around Dani, hunting for food. She barks and runs after Mamo, leaving Dani on his own.

ACT 2

● ●

SCENE 1

*A rubbish heap. The gang: **Million** the gang leader supervizes **Buffalo**, the tough one, **Shoes**, and **Karate**, the smallest of the gang, as they sift through the rubbish looking for anything of value. **Karate** looks ill. **Shoes**, who has a stammer, is surrounded by footwear. He tries some on and discards them. He sees one shoe near **Buffalo** and goes to get it. **Buffalo** shoves him away. **Karate** coughs.*

Million	Karate! Take a break.
Karate	I'm fine.
Million	Go and sit down.

*Getachew enters with **Mamo** and **Suri**.*

Getachew	Million! This is the guy I was telling you about.
Million	*[To **Getachew**]* Get to work.

Getachew goes to work on the dump.

Million	So you're Mamo.
Mamo	Yes, and this is my dog, Suri.

*Suri runs to the rubbish heap to play near **Buffalo**. **Buffalo** shoos her away. She growls at him and snaps at his feet.*

Karate	Here Suri!

*Suri runs to **Karate**. They play together.*

Million	Getachew told me you were kidnapped.
Mamo	That's right. This guy—
Million	Are you a thief? *[Looks at **Getachew**]*
Mamo	No! I'm not a thief.

47

Getachew	I swear it was Paul who stole the chewing gum from that store.
Buffalo	Oh, it's not Feleke this time?
Getachew	It's true!
Million	If you join us and you steal we will beat you and then we'll kick you out. Those are the rules. *[Looks at Suri]* Your dog's too small to guard our blankets when we're away.
	Suri whines.
Karate	I like her, Million.
Million	I guess you can train her.
	Suri barks joyfully.
Mamo	Are you saying I'm in?
Million	You'll stay with us for a week then we'll decide. You must obey all our rules. No thieving, no fighting. Share everything. Whatever you beg or earn you bring to me. Where I say go, you go. Where I say we sleep, you sleep. OK?
Mamo	Erm. The police are after me because I ran away.
Million	The farm is too far for them to come looking for you. The man who kidnapped you, was he your relative?
Mamo	He said he was my uncle but he was lying.
Million	You're safe. You'll get to know the rest of us later. Get to work.
	Mamo and Getachew high-five. Mamo offers his hand to Buffalo to shake. Buffalo glares at him. Getachew pulls him away from Buffalo.
Getachew	Steer clear of Buffalo. You can never tell what mood he's in.
	Shoes tries on another pair of battered shoes. Mamo finds an empty bottle.
Shoes	Are those trainers?
Mamo	It's a bottle. Man, you really like shoes.
Karate	Guess what we call him?

Shoes	My father said you can judge a man by his shoes.
	*Mamo goes close to **Buffalo**. **Buffalo** shoves him. **Suri** runs to **Mamo**'s defence, barking and growling at **Buffalo**.*
Mamo	Hey!
	***Karate** has a coughing fit. **Suri** whines concernedly. **Million** nods to **Shoes**. **Shoes** gets cough mixture. He hands it to **Million**. **Million** checks the contents. **Suri** runs in between **Mamo**'s legs, trying to guide him towards **Dani**.*
Million	*[Points to the collected stuff]* This won't fetch us enough for another bottle.
Buffalo	We'll have to go begging.
Million	*[Covers **Karate** in a blanket]* Tedros and his boys might have left the bridge.
Getachew	No way.
Buffalo	You should have let me at them. That was our patch.
Million	How's that going to help Karate?
Mamo	There's this kid I was hanging out with.
	***Suri** barks excitedly.*
Getachew	You cannot be serious.
Mamo	I want him to join us.
Million	Where is he?
Mamo	He's at the cemetery.
Shoes	The cemetery?
Getachew	He's some rich kid who ran away from his mansion.
Buffalo	No.
Shoes	He'll look down on us.
Mamo	He's not like that.
Getachew	I'm not prepared to be anyone's houseboy again.

Million	Sorry, Mamo.
	Suri whines.
Mamo	He's got money. We can use it to buy Karate his medicine.
Buffalo	'We'? You're not one of us yet.
Mamo	You helped me. Why shouldn't I help him?
Buffalo	You hear that? Mamo feels sorry for a rich kid. What are you, stupid?
Shoes	We don't want him! Wait. Has he got trainers?
	Karate's cough gets worse.
Million	You sure he's got enough for Karate's medicine?
Buffalo	Million!
Mamo	Yes.
	Suri barks.
Million	Bring him here.
	Mamo makes to run off. Suri tries to hurry Mamo to get Dani. She runs off.
	I want to see him first. If he's OK, fine. If not, he has to leave. OK?
Mamo	Thanks, Million. Hold on Suri! [Runs after Suri]

• •

SCENE 2

London. Ruth is wheeled into the operating theatre by a Nurse.

Addis Ababa. Paulos prays.

Paulos	Father, I pray that Ruth's operation is a success. And wherever Daniel is, please bring him back to me. I promise I will not beat him too hard. Only enough to make sure he never tries a stunt like this again. Amen.

SCENE 3

Outside a restaurant. The boys with **Mamo** *and* **Dani**. **Suri** *runs around* **Dani**'s *legs, happy to be reunited with him. The boys eye him coolly.*

Million	So, Dani, Mamo tells me the police are after you.
Dani	Yes. I just want you to hide me until my mother returns from London.
Million	We don't have a place to stay.
Shoes	Not any longer.
Dani	Where do you sleep?
Million	Here.
Shoes	Or there.
Getachew	Or over there.
Dani	You're homeless?
Buffalo	If you can't do without your bed, go to a hotel.

Suri growls at **Buffalo**.

Mikhail, **Dani**'s *uncle, passes by.*

Mikhail	Dani? Dani, is that you?

Dani *panics. He pulls his cap over his eyes.* **Mamo** *walks over to* **Mikhail**. *The boys hide* **Dani**.

Suri *tries to pull* **Dani** *towards* **Mikhail**.

Karate	No father, no mother. Very hungry. Give me one birr.
Mikhail	Dani!

Mamo *joins* **Karate** *to block off* **Mikhail**.

Mamo	No father, no mother. Very hungry. Give me one birr.

Mikhail *shrugs his shoulder. He walks off.*

Shoes	Who was that?
Dani	My uncle, Mikhail. Thanks for hiding me.
Million	So. You want protection.
Dani	Yes.
Million	That's all you'll get from us. What I told Mamo goes for you too. Anyone who steals will be caned and kicked out. You pull your weight when we go begging and scavenging. You do what you're told and you share whatever you make. *[Looks at **Dani**'s bag]* What belongs to one belongs to all.

Dani remains clutching his bag.

What belongs to one belongs to all.

Dani still doesn't get it. Mamo snatches Dani's bag.

Mamo	Dani has brought us some clothes to share.

*The boys cheer. **Buffalo** snatches the bag from **Mamo** and hands it to **Million**. **Million** returns the bag to **Dani**. **Dani** opens it. They crowd round **Dani** eagerly. **Million** takes the yellow shirt. **Mamo** looks at it longingly.*

Dani	That's for Mamo.

Dani shrinks as all eyes turn on him. Million approaches him, holding up the shirt. Dani gulps. Million hands the shirt to Mamo. The gang cheers. Dani watches in despair as Million gives his things away. Million gives a pair of trainers to Karate, Shoes is dismayed. Karate gives them to Shoes. Shoes yells with delight. Buffalo gets a shirt. He puts it on. He acts as if he hates the shirt. Then he breaks into a dance – he loves it! Karate gets a sweater. He hugs Dani. Dani, surprised, smiles at Karate. Karate coughs. They stop celebrating.

Million	Mamo says you have money.
Dani	Yes.
Million	Give Buffalo five birr to buy cough syrup for Karate.

Dani gives Buffalo the money.

Million	OK, guys. Lunchtime.

Dani bounds hungrily towards the restaurant.

Million	Dani! Where are you going?
Dani	For lunch.

The boys laugh at Dani's naivety. Dani is embarrassed.

Million	Listen, Dani …

Cook enters with a pot of scraps. He throws them into the dustbin.

Shoes	Guys. Guys!

They wait eagerly. Dani looks on bewildered. Cook goes back inside the restaurant. To Dani's horror, the boys rush to the dustbin and eat from it.

Mamo	Hey! There's still meat on this bone.

| Karate | This is a full roll of injera. Dani … [Gives **Suri** a piece. Offers the rest to **Dani**] |

Dani stands paralyzed.

It's OK. There's loads more here. Quick, before the other gangs arrive.

*Dani hesitates. He takes the injera between his thumb and forefinger. He nibbles a piece, disgusted. He watches the boys gobble the food. They are too hungry to notice him. Only **Shoes** looks up from his food to see **Dani**. **Dani** takes another nibble as his hunger gets the better of him. He gobbles the rest down. **Suri** barks angrily at him for not giving her a piece.*

| Dani | Sorry, Suri. |

Mamo gives *Suri* some food.

| Shoes | Now you're one of us. |

Buffalo glares at **Shoes**.

| Million | Are we done? |

*They nod. **Dani** looks longingly at the bin. He's still hungry.*

| Million | Back to work! |

*They run to the rubbish heap. **Dani** heaves after them. **Mamo** waits for him.*

| Dani | What are they … What are we looking for? |

| Mamo | Anything of value, Dani. |

*Dani hesitates. He sees **Million** looking at him. Gingerly he goes up the rubbish heap. He recoils from the stench. Holding his nose he pokes about. He steps back.*

Mind! [Pushes **Dani**. Picks up a shard of broken glass and shows it to **Dani**]

| Million | Careful there. |

Dani nods and returns to his scavenging. Mamo finds a hat, a flask and a plastic bottle.

Mamo	*[To Dani]* You'll never find anything useful like that. Dig deeper.

Dani tries but is useless at scavenging.

Million	Gather!

The boys gather around Million with their collection. Dani looks worried. He has collected nothing. It's nearly his turn. Mamo slips him the plastic bottle.

Million	Dani.

Dani proffers the plastic bottle.

Million	This is all?

Dani stands sheepishly. The boys look at him with disdain.

Mamo	It's useful.

Million shakes his head. He shifts through the items. He picks up a flask.

Million	Who found this?

The boys point to Mamo. Million picks up a hat.

Shoes	Mamo found that too.
Million	Mamo! *[Tries the hat]* This is a hat for a joviro. I name you City Rat.

The boys are about to cheer. Mamo raises his hand in indignation.

Mamo	Another name, please!
Million	How about the Hyena!
Mamo	No animal names!
Million	I got it. The Garbage King!

Mamo   Garbage King. Yeah. I like it.

*The boys sing as they dance around **Mamo**. **Dani** joins in. He is awkward. **Suri** gets in everyone's way. **Mamo**'s spirits lift. He starts singing. The boys are impressed with his singing. As he sings, as if by magic, he finds more stuff of value on the rubbish heap.*

Million   All hail Mamo.

All   The Garbage King!

• •

SCENE 4

*Dani's house. **Paulos** is talking on his mobile phone.*

Paulos   But you told me it was a routine procedure. OK, OK. How long before you will know? Oh God. All right. Thank you. *[Hangs up. Puts his head in his hands]*

*Ato Mesfin, **Dani**'s teacher, enters.*

Ato Mesfin   Good day, sir.

Paulos   Good day. And you are?

Ato Mesfin	I am Ato Mesfin, Dani's teacher. I was passing by.
Paulos	I apologize for sounding so harsh. My wife.
Ato Mesfin	Dani mentioned she was ill.
Paulos	You saw Dani?
Ato Mesfin	Before you withdrew him from school.
Paulos	Oh.
Ato Mesfin	Please give *Woizero** Ruth my best wishes.
Paulos	Thank you, Ato Mesfin. What can I do for you?
Ato Mesfin	I came to find out how Dani is doing. His friends ask after him.
Paulos	They do?
Ato Mesfin	He was my best student.
Paulos	What subjects do you teach?
Ato Mesfin	Amharic and History.
Paulos	So you are the teacher who encourages my son to daydream and write stories.
Ato Mesfin	I encourage all my students to work hard. Dani is very good at telling stories.
Paulos	That's why you miss him. He's the only one who takes your classes seriously.
Ato Mesfin	Have you read his work? He takes our history and myths and creates new and exciting stories with them. He told this story about King Menelik—
Paulos	Please leave. *[Gestures to **Ato Mesfin** to leave]*
	***Ato Mesfin** doesn't know what to say. He exits.*
	***Paulos** gets on his phone.*
Paulos	Hello, Inspector … No, I don't want excuses. Find my son!

---
* 'Woizero' can be translated as 'Madam'.

SCENE 5

*Outside the restaurant. The boys, apart from **Buffalo**. They are all hungry. They bring all their money together in front of **Million**. **Mamo** peers inside the dustbin. **Suri** whines with hunger.*

Million   This isn't enough to buy a slice of injera.

Getachew   You mean we have to eat from the dustbin again? Uh!

Shoes   Next time we should fight back instead of letting Kelile's boys kick us off the dump. We're getting a reputation as pushovers.

Million   What did you do when Tedros kicked us off our patch?

Shoes   I didn't run away. I went to get a stick.

Karate   And you went all the way to Mamo's farm to get it?

Shoes   Shut up you little ant. It's because of you we keep getting pushed around.

Karate   Don't blame your cowardice on me.

Shoes   *[Angry, approaches **Karate**]* Who are you calling a coward?

Million   Enough, you two!

Cook enters with a pot of scraps. The boys wait hungrily for him to scrape out every last scrap.

Dani   I'll share some with you this time, Suri.

Cook takes his time.

Getachew   *[Impatiently]* Come on!

*Cook looks at them. They look the other way, pretending to take in the air. At last! **Cook** goes back into the kitchen. As the boys rush to the dustbin, a **Policeman** appears. He looks at **Dani**. He brings out a photograph, then looks at **Dani** again. **Mamo** sees him.*

Mamo   Dani …

Getachew finds a glorious chunk of meat.

Policeman   *[To **Dani**]* Hey you. Come here.

Dani is scared. Apart from Getachew the boys retreat.

I said come here!

The Policeman comes towards them. They run. Getachew is about to bite into the meat when Shoes drags him away. Getachew drops the meat on the ground. Suri picks it up and runs away. They lose the Policeman. They laugh at their success in evading him. Buffalo enters with the blankets.

Buffalo	What's up?
Mamo	A policeman recognized Dani. We dodged him.

Getachew looks enviously at Suri gnawing away at the meat.

Shoes	*[Laughs]* Look at Getachew's mouth!
Buffalo	So we're going to bed hungry because of you.
Mamo	It wasn't his fault. The cook took forever to bring the food out.
Buffalo	I wasn't talking to you, Dani's houseboy.
Million	Leave it, Buffalo.

Buffalo hands out the blankets. They bed down for the night. Buffalo signals to Million. They exit. In the background we see them drinking heavily on the heap. Getachew falls asleep, moaning with hunger. Shoes brings out a handkerchief and sniffs it. His eyes glaze over. Mamo sits next to Dani and Karate. Karate coughs for a long while.

Dani	You OK?
Karate	Yeah.
Dani	Karate? What's your real name?
Karate	I don't know. My mother died when I was a baby.
Dani	So who looked after you?
Karate	Some other mothers. They were street beggars too.
Mamo	*[Takes Suri and puts her inside his blanket]* Where are those other mothers of yours now?

ACT 2   SCENE 5

59

Karate	Gone. The nicest one fell sick and died. Then I fell sick. That's when Million found me and took me to the clinic. I've been with him ever since. He's my big brother. It's nice to have someone looking out for you.
Mamo	Yes, it is.
Karate	I thought Million was going to buy *tej** when you gave him the money for my medicine. I wouldn't have minded. I like tej.
Dani	You mustn't drink tej at your age.
Karate	It helps me sleep. Anyway, Million doesn't let me drink it anymore. I wish he'd stop drinking it too. He's not nice when he's drunk. Thanks for the shirt, Dani. It's the best present I've ever had.
Dani	If you can't sleep I can tell you a story.
Karate	Yes!
Dani	Once upon a time there was a baby leopard that had lost her mother …

*Karate snuggles up to **Dani**. **Mamo** smiles. **Karate** has a coughing fit. **Million** and **Buffalo** awake from their drunken stupor and come to the rest of the boys. **Shoes** remains in his daze. **Million** feels **Karate**'s head.*

Million	Buffalo, take him to the hospital.
Karate	I'm fine. *[Continues coughing]*
Buffalo	Come on. *[Lifts **Karate** up]*
Karate	I said I'm fine.
Million	Just for a check-up. You'll stay with him and bring him back, Buffalo. Go on.

*Buffalo puts **Karate** on his back and exits. **Million** returns to his drink on the heap. He holds the bottle to his lips. He does not drink it. He pours it away.*

---

* 'Tej' is an alcoholic drink.

Getachew	He hates being away from us. The first time he was admitted he ran away.
Dani	You should have taken him straight back.
Mamo	You remember I told you how the Farmer beat me? I said I made up the bit about me eating those leaves?
Dani	You really ate them?
Mamo	I survived only because Hailu and Yohannes found me. It was soon after I got better that I ran away. I was lucky, a kind lorry driver brought me back to Addis. So I understand why Karate doesn't want to be left on his own with strangers.
Dani	But it's not the same thing.
Mamo	Maybe this is too complicated for you …
	Million returns to the boys.
Million	Stop talking and go to bed. We have to be at the dump very early tomorrow.
	Dani and Mamo look at each other. They turn over on opposite sides and sleep.

• •

SCENE 6

Awassa. Tiggist hangs out washing from a bucket similar to the one Mamo found. Salma enters. Tiggist looks at her hopefully.

Salma	Sorry, Tiggist. My friend couldn't find Mamo.
	Tiggist sighs.
	I'm sure he's fine. Boys his age look after themselves all the time.
Tiggist	I remember once when he was a toddler. My friend was plaiting my hair in the yard. I took my eye off him. I found him down the road trying to buy sweets. He wanted to pay the trader with some old newspaper.
Salma	You'll soon be back in Addis, then you can look for him.

Yacob enters.

Yacob   Salma!

*Salma goes over to him. They chat briefly. **Tiggist** steals glances at **Yacob**. Their eyes meet. She looks away. **Salma** returns, dragging **Yacob** along with her.*

Salma   Tiggist, meet Yacob. Yacob, Tiggist.

*Salma shoves **Yacob** into **Tiggist**.*

Tiggist   Nice to meet you.

Yacob   Nice to meet you too. My sister has been telling me all about you.

Tiggist   You are brother and sister?

Salma   Yacob's a trained electrician. He is hoping to set up a repair shop here in Awassa.

Yacob   I'd better be on my way. I will come by this time tomorrow.

Salma   Tomorrow then.

Yacob   Goodbye Tiggist.

Tiggist   Goodbye.

Yacob exits.

Salma   So you'll definitely be seeing more of him, eh?

Mrs Faridah *[Off]* Salma!

Salma   Yes madam! *[Runs off]*

*Tiggist breaks into a dance, daydreaming of **Yacob**. She picks up the bucket. It reminds her of **Mamo**. She sighs.*

• •

SCENE 7

*On the boys' patch of the heap, Addis Ababa. By a gutter. The boys wash their bodies and their clothes in the gutter. **Dani** looks on embarrassed and disgusted. The boys react to the dirty, cold water,* *making a bath even less enticing for **Dani**. **Suri** splashes about in the water. She pulls at **Mamo**'s clothes.*

Million [To **Dani**] You don't know when you'll get another chance to clean your clothes.

***Dani** wades in gently. He washes his clothes clumsily. **Suri** pulls at his clothes. The boys look at **Dani**, shaking their heads.*

Mamo [To **Dani**] Watch.

Dani I thought Tiggist washed your clothes for you.

Mamo Are you watching?

Dani [Copies **Mamo**] I didn't mean to annoy you last night. I was only thinking—

Mamo Don't worry about it.

***Dani** is unsure.*

Mamo It's OK, Dani, honest.

***Buffalo** enters, sad.*

Million Buffalo, what's up?

Buffalo It's Karate. He's been admitted.

Million [Puts on his shirt, wet] Mamo and Dani, stay and look after our stuff.

Mamo We're coming with you.

Buffalo They won't let us see him now. Visiting hours are in the afternoon.

Million [Thinks] OK. I'll go and get us some bread. Get up to the heap. Garbage King, you lead the search. Getachew, come with me.

***Million** and **Getachew** exit.*

Buffalo What did he say?

Dani He said Mamo is in charge—

Mamo	He meant I was in charge of the search. I know you are second in command.
Buffalo	Get up there. *[Grabs **Dani**]* Don't you ever talk to me unless I talk to you, you hear? *[Shoves **Dani** away]*

*Dani goes to work beside **Mamo**.*

Dani	I was only trying to explain. Why does he hate me?
Shoes	His mother was a maid for this rich guy. When the wife was out he got her pregnant. He denied it and she was kicked out onto the street.
Dani	So you're saying Buffalo … ?
Shoes	*[Nods]* Is some rich man's son. So don't bother trying to make friends with him. It isn't going to happen.

*The boys sift through the rubbish. **Mamo** as usual seems to magically find useful stuff. **Shoes** is stabbed by a syringe.*

	Ow!
Buffalo	Shoes?
Shoes	I'm all right. It's nothing. *[Sucks his palm. Throws the syringe away]*

*Dani finds a notebook and a plastic bag. He puts the notebook into it. **Buffalo** snatches the bag from him. He brings out the notebook.*

Buffalo	This is all you've found?
Dani	I'm still searching.
Buffalo	You went to one of those posh schools, yeah? The ones with the white uniforms and brown sandals. I bet you had a driver to take you to school.
Mamo	Leave him alone.
Buffalo	Why are you really here? You want to see how we animals live?
Mamo	He's not like that.

Buffalo	How long have you known him for? You act like you're his best friend. You are nothing but riff-raff to him. Oh, you think once he gets tired of slumming it he will take you away with him?
Mamo	He needed my help.
Buffalo	That's right, you're his 'helper'. You're helping him treat us like his servants. That is why since morning the only thing he has found is this rubbish! *[About to tear it]*

Dani stands petrified. Mamo lunges at Buffalo. Buffalo throws Mamo to the ground. He holds Mamo in a lock. Mamo bites his arm. Buffalo yells and lets go of Mamo. Mamo readies himself to fend off another attack. Buffalo looks at his arm, enraged. He is about to lunge at Mamo again. Million enters with a bag of bread rolls. He stands in between them.

Million	Stop that! *[To Mamo]* New boy, what did I tell you about fighting? You ever raise your fists to anyone of us you are gone. You hear? *You hear?*

Mamo stands panting, his fists still raised.

	Leave. Go on!
Buffalo	I started it.
Million	You started it? Why?
Buffalo	He got on my nerves, him and that fat parasite.
Mamo	He is not a parasite.
Million	Hey! That's enough. *[Takes Buffalo aside]* Buffalo, what's up, man?
Buffalo	You know me. What with Karate falling ill and look what the rich kid found all day. *[Shows him a notebook]*

Million flicks through it.

	See? There aren't even any words in it. We can't sell it.
Dani	I was going to use it to write my stories in.

Million	And what good are your stories to us? *[Drops it]* Come on, let's eat. Where's Getachew?
	Dani picks up the notebook.
Shoes	He was with you.
Million	He went on ahead of me. Save some for him.
	*Dani crouches next to **Mamo**. They are apart from the gang.*
Dani	For a minute Million sounded like my dad. I hope Buffalo didn't hurt you.
Mamo	I'm OK. I know kung fu.
	*Million shares the food. **Mamo** collects his share. **Dani** stays where he is. **Mamo** takes **Dani**'s portion to him.*
Buffalo	Servant.
Mamo	Shut up.
	Buffalo stands up.
Million	Buffalo! Sit and eat.
	*Before a morsel is eaten **Getachew** comes racing round the corner.*
Getachew	Guys, police!
	*The boys drop their food and hide among the rubbish. **Dani** brings up the rear, panting heavily. He looks around panicked. **Mamo** pops up and drags him into the rubbish. A **Policeman** runs in. He looks around but he cannot find them. He exits. The boys emerge from their hiding places.*
Million	Are we all here?
	They look around. They are all here. They nod.
Getachew	Wow. That was close, man.
Million	Why were the police after you?
Getachew	They were after Dani.
Million	How could they know he was with you?

Getachew	I mean they were after us.
Million	No. You came running—
Getachew	To tell you they were coming.
Million	They've never come after us for no reason.
Getachew	Maybe they thought we were some other gang.
Million	Where did you disappear to? I turned round and you weren't there anymore.
Getachew	I saw a mate passing by. I went to say hello.
Million	You went off without telling me?
Getachew	I didn't think I'd be that long with him.
Million	Empty your pockets.
Getachew	What?
Million	You heard me.
Getachew	Hey Million, come on, man.
Million	Your pockets, Getachew.
Getachew	It's me, Getachew. You can't treat me this way.

Buffalo and *Shoes* *hold his arms.*

Hey!

Million *goes through* *Getachew's pockets. He brings out a packet of cigarettes and a lighter.*

I found them in the dustbin outside the shop.

Million	The seal isn't broken. You stole them from the shop.
Getachew	I didn't! Honest, Million—
Million	You're a thief. We don't have thieves with us.
Getachew	I'm not a thief. I found them.
Million	You're out, Getachew.

Getachew	Million.
Million	I told you this was your last chance.
Getachew	I scavenged them. How can a shop owner leave them in the open?
Million	We take what people leave behind. We don't go into shops and take what does not belong to us.
Getachew	And what do people leave behind? Rubbish! When will it be my turn to have something good?
Million	Make sure you don't return to our patch to steal our blankets.
Getachew	You can't make me leave. We made you the leader. I made you leader. You and your stupid rules.
Million	Hands up all in favour of Getachew leaving.

*One by one they all raise their hands, except for **Dani** and **Mamo**. The other gang members look at them. Slowly, with a sense of betrayal, **Mamo** raises his hand.*

Getachew	Mamo! I brought you in. Mamo!
Million	We have spoken as one.
Getachew	Million, I was joking.
Buffalo	You heard Million. Leave!

Buffalo and Shoes grab Getachew.

Getachew	Please, Million. I have nowhere to go. I'm sorry. It was a mistake. Please take me back. Please! I'll never steal again. I'm sorry. I'm sorry …
Million	You want to stay with us.
Getachew	Yes! Yes, I do.
Million	What if you steal again? What if we get arrested again because of you and get beaten up at the police station?
Getachew	I won't do it again. I swear to God.

Million signals. Getachew takes off his shirt. Buffalo pushes him down on his knees. Shoes gets a stick and gives it to Buffalo. Buffalo flogs Getachew. Mamo cannot bear it. He grabs the stick off Buffalo.

Mamo Enough, Million. Please.

Buffalo looks to Million. Million nods.

Million Your last chance, Getachew. Steal again and you're out.

Getachew I won't steal again, Million, I promise.

Million walks off. The boys follow him, except for Mamo and Getachew. Mamo picks up Getachew's shirt and hands it to him.

Mamo Getachew.

Getachew *[Snatches the shirt off Mamo]* Get lost, Mamo!

Mamo looks sadly at Getachew. Getachew, in pain, slowly puts on his shirt.

Mamo exits.

ACT 3

• •

SCENE 1

Split stage:
*London. **Ruth** in a hospital bed, sleeping. A **Nurse** comes in and checks her temperature. She moves **Ruth** offstage.*

*Addis. Outside a hospital, **Mamo** watches over **Suri**. Inside, **Dani**, **Million**, **Buffalo**, **Getachew** and **Shoes** huddle around **Karate**'s bed. They are awkward in the hospital surroundings, except for **Dani**. **Shoes** shows off his newly bandaged hand to the boys. **Karate** is wearing the shirt **Dani** gave him. His hospital pyjamas are on the chair next to his bed. A bell rings: visiting hours are over.*

Karate	You said I could leave with you!
Million	I know but the doctor said—
Karate	Look at me. I'm OK.
Million	*[Takes **Karate**'s shirt off and puts his pyjamas back on]* We don't want the nurse to chase us out.

***Karate** weeps.*

Million	Hey. Hey! We'll be back tomorrow.
Dani	Concentrate on getting better. You'll be discharged sooner.
Getachew	When they discharge you, see if they'll let you take the pillow.
Million	Come on guys. Tomorrow, Karate.

*They go outside. **Mamo** jumps up.*

Dani	So when did the doctor say they're letting him out, Million?
Million	He said the medicine isn't working.
Dani	What did he mean by that?
Million	Karate is not going to recover.

The boys are crestfallen.

70

Dani	Poor Karate.

*Mamo sneaks into the hospital. He throws **Karate**'s shirt to him. **Karate** puts it on. Stealthily he carries **Karate** out of the hospital. **Mamo** and **Karate** stand before the gang. **Million** looks at **Karate** for a split second then scoops him up. **Getachew** throws **Mamo** a conciliatory smile. **Million** runs off with **Karate**. The boys follow. **Dani** pulls **Mamo** aside.*

What did you do that for? We can't look after him.

Mamo	I thought you understood.
Dani	How is he going to get better?
Mamo	But he's not going to get better, is he?
Dani	You want him to die?
Mamo	Of course not! Why would you say something like that? If it were your mother, would you want her to die alone in London without seeing you again?
Dani	You know what I mean.
Mamo	No I don't know what you mean, Dani. OK?

*Mamo walks ahead, leaving **Dani** behind.*

• •

SCENE 2

*Awassa. **Tiggist** and **Yacob** by a lake. **Tiggist** is amazed by its beauty.*

Tiggist	It's beautiful. I never thought I'd ever like Awassa. Now I don't want to leave.
Yacob	You don't have to, Tiggist.
Tiggist	Mrs Faridah is returning to Addis on Saturday.
Yacob	Ah.
Tiggist	I have to look after Yasmin. And I have to find my brother. I haven't heard from him since I came here.

Yacob	So. Saturday.
Tiggist	Yes.
Yacob	It's only three days away.
Tiggist	I know.

Pause. **Yacob** *musters up the courage.*

Yacob	Tiggist.
Tiggist	Yes?
Yacob	I can't … What I mean to say is, I'm not ready yet. I still don't earn much money. We couldn't, you know, not until I've got my shop.
Tiggist	Yes, I'll wait. I'll wait until you're ready.
Yacob	*[Brings out a piece of paper]* This is the phone number of my neighbour. I'm around in the evenings. If you call, he will send someone to get me.

Tiggist *takes the number.*

Goodbye, Tiggist. For now. *[Exits]*

Tiggist *looks at the paper. She sighs. She already misses* **Yacob**.

● ●

SCENE 3

The boys' patch at the rubbish heap. The boys surround **Karate**. *He is feeling much worse.* **Dani** *and* **Mamo** *sit at opposites ends.* **Million** *tries to make* **Karate** *eat some food.* **Shoes'** *bandage is dirty.* **Dani** *feeds* **Suri**.

Million	You have to eat, Karate. You've not taken anything since you left the hospital.
Karate	*[He can barely talk]* I just want water.
Million	*[To* **Dani***]* You say you know stories. *[Makes room for* **Dani** *to sit beside* **Karate***]* Tell him one.

Karate *cheers weakly.*

Dani	*[Sits beside **Karate**]* There's one about the bird and the elephant. Then there's one about the King and the flute. There's also one about the brother and sister.
Karate	The brother and sister.
	*They gather round **Dani** except for **Buffalo** whose back is turned to them. **Suri** also listens. **Karate** smiles.*
Dani	Once upon a time there was a boy and a girl who lived all on their own.
Shoes	Were they living in Addis?
Dani	I don't know. Anyway this hyena—
Shoes	Then it was in the country. You saw hyenas in the country, didn't you, Mamo?
Dani	This hyena cooked food for them and left it at their doorstep. Every night they would eat the food but they didn't know who left it for them.
	Karate closes his eyes.
Getachew	A hyena leaving food. That must be the only kind hyena in the world.
Dani	She wasn't doing it out of kindness. She wanted to trick them and eat them.
Shoes	If she was hungry why didn't she just eat the food she cooked?
Buffalo	*[Without turning round]* Shut up and let him tell his story.
Dani	So one day the boy hid in a tree and saw the hyena bringing the food. The hyena saw him and called him down from the tree. She said, 'You are such a handsome boy. I want to marry you. I will keep you safe and you'll never ever be hungry again …'
	Karate's head slumps.
Million	Karate? Karate!

*Karate is dead. **Million** wails. The boys sing a dirge*, led by **Mamo**. **Municipal Workers** appear. They put **Karate** on a stretcher.*

Worker 1	*[Brings out a pen and notepad]* We'll need a name for our burial records.
Million	We knew him only as Karate.
Worker 1	OK. What about his father's name?

The boys look at each other.

Dani	Million. His father's name is Million.

*Worker 1 writes. He puts away his pen and notebook. With Worker 2 he lifts **Karate** and takes him away. **Million** is inconsolable. **Shoes** puts his arm round **Million**'s shoulder. He shrugs it off and walks away. **Buffalo** goes after him, followed by **Shoes** and **Getachew**. **Mamo** makes to follow.*

Mamo.

Mamo stops. He doesn't turn round.

I need to know what's happened to my mother.

Mamo	I thought you said she was in London.
Dani	Yes but my father will have news of her. I need to know if she is all right.
Mamo	And you want me to find out for you?
Dani	Yes. Please.
Mamo	How do I do that?
Dani	If you go to my house ask Negussie. He's our gateman. You can't miss him. He has one eye.
Mamo	Your gateman has only one eye?

They look at each other for a second. They burst out laughing.

---

* A 'dirge' is a sad song usually sung at a funeral.

Dani	There's a sweet seller near to my house. Negussie talks to her all the time. Ask her. She'll know. I'll lead you up to the street. Thanks, Mamo.
Mamo	It's OK.

They put their arms around each other and exit.

● ●

SCENE 4

*Outside **Dani**'s house. **Mamo** looks around, daunted by the wealth he sees around him. He sees the **Sweet Seller**. He walks up to her.*

Mamo	Could you let me have a cup of water? For the sake of Jesus.

*Sweet Seller gives him a cup of water. **Mamo** drains the cup.*

	Thank you. *[Looks around]* I'm lost. I'm looking for the church of St. Raphael.
Sweet Seller	You are more than lost! Turn back where you were coming from and do a left up the hill.
Mamo	Ah, yes. The lady said it was up a hill.
Sweet Seller	What lady?
Mamo	She lives near here. She gave me money for my sick mother. She didn't look well herself. She said she was going abroad for an operation. I promised to pray for her at any church she liked that the operation would go smoothly.
Sweet Seller	Ah, you are talking about Woizero Ruth, poor lady.
Mamo	That's her! Woizero Ruth. Do you know if she's returned?
Sweet Seller	She has gone to a greater place I'm afraid.
Mamo	You mean she has passed away?
Sweet Seller	I saw visitors dressed in black coming and going all day out of the house.
Mamo	Poor Dani.
Sweet Seller	What did you say?

Mamo	I said I will pray for her soul.
Sweet Seller	Their gateman told me something has happened to the master's son. He goes out every day looking like thunder. I knew already something was wrong since he stopped coming to buy sweets. He's my best customer.
Mamo	Thank you. *[Sighs]*

Sweet Seller exits.

The boys, singing, appear on the rubbish heap scavenging for stuff. **Dani** *finds a pen. He checks that it works and pockets it.* **Suri** *sees* **Mamo** *and runs to him.* **Dani** *runs over to him. We see* **Mamo** *telling* **Dani** *the bad news.* **Dani**'s *face drops. The singing stops as the boys notice* **Dani**'s *reaction. They gather round him.*

	I'll go back. I'll ask your gateman, just to make sure.
Dani	I just want to be on my own.

The boys return to the rubbish heap. **Mamo** *stays with* **Dani***. He sits down next to him.*

Mamo	Look, why don't you go and see your father? He will want you to be together.
Dani	My mother was the only reason why he hadn't tried to send me to Feisal until now. With her gone, he'll be ten times worse.
Mamo	He's your father.
Dani	And I hate him! I hate him. *[Sobs]* I hate him.

Mamo *hugs* **Dani***.*

In the background we see **Paulos***, dressed in black. He accepts the sympathies of a* **Guest***, also dressed in black. He sighs.*

• •

SCENE 5

The boys' patch at the rubbish heap. **Suri** *guards their blankets. A street kid enters. He tries to steal a blanket.* **Suri** *chases after him. The boys return.* **Mamo** *pats* **Suri***.*

Shoes	*[Hands **Buffalo** a few coins]* This is all I got.
	***Buffalo** looks dismayed.*
Getachew	I didn't get much for the plastics. *[Hands money to **Million**]*
Million	Two birr? That's all he paid you? Everybody up. Up! To the church. Make sure you beg like you've never begged before.
	***Dani** stays where he is. **Million** looks at him.*
Dani	I can't go to the church. I'll be recognized.
	The boys gesture and mumble in annoyance.
Million	You can't scavenge; you refuse to beg. But you can eat our food.
Buffalo	That's why he's rich. He eats off others.
Million	Let's go. Let's leave Prince Dani.
	*They leave. **Mamo** casts a long glance at **Dani**. **Dani** looks to him for support. **Mamo** shrugs helplessly and exits after the gang.*
Dani	At least you're useful for something. *[Pats **Suri**]*
	***Dani** brings out the pen from his chest pocket. He takes the notebook. He thinks for a moment. He begins to write.*
	'The Wicked Hyena'.
	***Suri** sees a pigeon. She chases after it offstage. **Dani** does not see her leave.*
	*The boys return with two bags of food. **Dani** sits up.*
Mamo	Where is Suri?
	***Dani** looks around.*
Mamo	Suri! Suri! *[Exits]*
	*They sit together and lay out the food. **Dani** joins them. They ignore him. **Mamo** comes back with **Suri**. There are feathers in her mouth. **Mamo** glares at **Dani**. **Dani** looks apologetic.*

Mamo	She was miles away down the road.
Million	You don't do anything else. The least you could have done was look after Suri.
Getachew	Oh no. *[Snatches the notebook out of **Dani**'s hand]* Our little prince has been busy writing. What's this rubbish?
	*Million snatches it from **Getachew**.*
Dani	It's 'The Wicked Hyena'. It's a good story.
Million	I'll show you what it's good for. *[About to rip up the notebook]*
Dani	No! Stop! Please. You could tear out the pages and sell them. Sell the story I mean.
Million	Who is going to buy your stories?
Dani	Please, Million, why not try?
Buffalo	Waste of time.
Getachew	He'll come up with anything so as not to beg.
Million	Who wants to sell Dani's stories?
	They all turn away.
Mamo	I'll sell them.
Buffalo	Dani's servant.
Mamo	Keep saying that. It means nothing to me.
	*Mamo takes the notebook. He tears out two pages. He passes by **Dani**. **Dani** smiles his appreciation at **Mamo**.*
Million	Wait! If you do not sell that story, your friend here has to leave.
	The boys cheer.
Dani	That's not fair.
Million	That's the deal.
Mamo	Come on, Suri!
	*Mamo and **Suri** exit.*

Million	Who will buy that nonsense?
Shoes	I would, if I could read.
Getachew	But you can't, can you?
Buffalo	Why don't we just dump him in front of his father's house now?

Shoes goes into a corner and brings out his handkerchief. Dani is left on his own.

Getachew	Yeah! We should …

Feleke passes by.

Feleke! If I catch you! *[Chases after him]*

• •

SCENE 6

Dani's house. Paulos is preparing to go out. Ato Mesfin enters warily.

Paulos	Ato Mesfin. Did I not tell you never to come here again?
Ato Mesfin	*[Hands Paulos Dani's story]* I recognized the handwriting.

Paulos	*[Goes through it]* Where is he? Take me to him! Right now!
Ato Mesfin	I take it Dani's not with Feisal.
Paulos	Do not play games with me, Ato Mesfin.
Ato Mesfin	I am not the one playing games, sir. I bought this off a street child. By the time I recognized the handwriting as Dani's the boy was gone.

Paulos sits down heavily.

Paulos	He's been missing since his mother went to London. I've searched everywhere for him. But this. *[Holds up the pages]* This means he is in Addis. Ato Mesfin, you must take me to the child you bought this story from.
Ato Mesfin	I know these children. We cannot just approach them without knowing what we're dealing with.
Paulos	He's my son. I'll take the lead.
Ato Mesfin	Do you really want to find Dani, sir?

Pause. Paulos relents.

Paulos	I suppose you know this environment better.
Ato Mesfin	Very good, sir. We will take your car. I know where to start looking for him.

Paulos picks up his stick.

Ato Mesfin	Sir!

Paulos puts down the stick. They exit.

● ●

SCENE 7

The boys' patch at the rubbish heap. Mamo back with the boys.

Shoes	You're lying.

Mamo hands the money to Million.

Million	*[Impressed]* Who did you sell it to?

Mamo	A teacher coming out of his school. He bought it from me. Two birr, man!

Million pats Dani on the shoulder. Dani hugs Mamo.

Million	What are you waiting for? Get writing!

Getachew runs in.

Getachew	Mamo! Your sister's back from Awassa.
Mamo	How do you know?
Getachew	I went begging near her shop. She's there man.

Mamo looks at Million.

Million	Go.

Mamo runs off. Dani looks after him.

● ●

SCENE 8

Mrs Faridah's shop.

Tiggist, sullen, minding the store. She looks at the paper with Yacob's phone number written on it. She puts the paper in her pocket.

Mamo enters.

Tiggist	*[Does not recognize Mamo]* Go away!
Mamo	And you said Mrs Faridah wouldn't mind me staying with you.
Tiggist	Mamo? Is that you? Oh my God. What happened to you? I searched all over for you. I went back to the old house, you weren't there. No one knew where you went.
Mamo	So you did leave me.
Tiggist	*[Hurt]* How do you think I could leave you, and then not try to find you? I was worried sick every day. All I could think about in Awassa was you.
Mamo	You really mean it?

Tiggist	Of course I mean it!

Yacob enters.

Yacob	Tiggist!
Tiggist	Yacob!

*They hug each other. **Mamo** looks at them in surprise.*

Tiggist	I've been phoning and phoning! Your neighbour said—
Yacob	Yes, I'm in Addis now. I didn't give him my address here to give to you and I forgot to get your address off Salma. I'm lucky I found you.
Tiggist	I thought you'd found someone else.

Mamo feels frozen out.

Yacob	Don't be silly. I've got a cousin here. He sells building materials. He wants me to help him build up the electrical side of the business. Do you know what that means? In a year or two we could be married!

*They hug. **Mamo** starts to walk away.*

Tiggist	I'd like you to meet my brother, Mamo. Mamo! Where are you going?
Yacob	Mamo, pleased to meet you. *[Offers his hand]*
Mamo	*[Wipes his hand on his shirt. Shakes **Yacob**'s hand]* Hello. I've got to go. My friends will be wondering where I am.
Tiggist	Just a minute, Yacob. *[She draws nearer to **Mamo**]*
Mamo	I wasn't the only one you were thinking of in Awassa.
Tiggist	Don't be like that. Yacob is a nice man. He'll look after us. We'll be a family.
Mamo	I've got friends looking after me. They're my family now.
Tiggist	I'm still your sister!

Mamo	I'll see you later, Tiggist.
Tiggist	Give me your address. I'll come see you.
Mamo	I'll come by again tomorrow. *[Exits]*
	Tiggist *looks after him.*
Yacob	What happened to him?
Tiggist	I don't know. It doesn't look good.
Yacob	If there's anything I can do to help him.
Tiggist	Thank you, Yacob. You don't realize how much that means to me.
	Yacob *hugs her. She looks over his shoulder as* ***Mamo*** *disappears into the distance.*

● ●

SCENE 9

	By the restaurant. The boys except for ***Buffalo***. ***Shoes'*** *hand is bandaged with a dirty linen.* ***Suri*** *plays around them.*
Million	There's no point in you following us.
Dani	I'm not going to beg. I'll stand afar off. I just need a break from writing.
Getachew	You don't need to hide. Your mother won't recognize you.
	They laugh and go off to beg. ***Mamo*** *enters.*
Dani	Mamo! Did you see Tiggist?
Mamo	Yes. She's become a woman now.
	Merga *enters, driving an expensive car.*
Dani	What makes you say that?
Million	Rich kid, you are so slow! It means she's got a man.
Mamo	I think they're going to get married. I don't think she'll take me back.

Dani	Of course she will.
	Merga gets out of the car. He is dressed in an expensive caftan*.
Mamo	I don't want to go back to her, anyway.
Shoes	You've been sniffing petrol fumes.
Million	Your sister's not a child. You're not going to be a kid forever either.
Dani	I'd give anything to see Meseret again.
Million	Mamo, you will go back to her and let her explain herself to you. And you will listen to her. You hear?
Mamo	Yes, boss.
Million	Give me a life other than this, I will grab it with my arms, my legs, my teeth—
	Mamo sees Merga. Merga enters a restaurant.
Mamo	Oh my God. It's him!
Dani	Who?
Mamo	The guy that kidnapped me. That's him entering the restaurant! *[Makes for the restaurant]*
	Dani holds him back.
Dani	Hold on, Mamo.
	Buffalo returns, with a shopping bag.
Dani	Mamo's seen the guy who kidnapped him.
Million	Where?
Mamo	*[Points]* In there! I'm going to kill him!
	Buffalo grabs him.
Buffalo	Cool down, my friend.

---

* A 'caftan' is a long loose robe.

Mamo calms down.

Million	That is his car, right? Go to the rubbish heap and find me all the sharp nails and pikes you can find. Quick! Before he returns.

From the rubbish they pick out nails and other sharp objects. They run back with their finds. They hammer them into the car tyres.

Merga enters. He sees the damage.

Merga	My car!
Million	Oh, look at your tyres. All four of them punctured at the same time.
Buffalo	We can help you replace them.
Merga	I don't need your help. *[Notices Mamo scowling at him. He does not recognize him]*
Million	How are you going to drive out of here?
Merga	Are you threatening me?
Million	Me threaten you, Uncle? We know a tyre dealer. He'll get you a good price for your tyres. Give my friend a birr to look after your car. We'll take you to buy the tyres.

Merga reluctantly gives Dani a birr note. Dani stands by the car. Million and the boys lead Merga away.

Mamo	We can't just take money off him. We have to make sure he never kidnaps another child again.

Dani brings out a marker. He writes on the side of Merga's car.

	What are you writing? What does it say?
Dani	'This man is a slaver. He steals boys and sells them.'
Mamo	Add, 'God will punish this man. He will run but he will never escape from justice.'

Dani writes it.

Mamo sees *Merga* coming back with the boys. He warns *Dani*. They hide behind the car. *Merga* and the boys enter. The boys are carrying tyres.

Million   I told you you'd get a good deal.

Merga sees the writing. He freezes.

Merga   What is this? Who did this to my car?

Million and the boys hesitate. They do not understand what is written on the car. *Dani* and *Mamo* come out of hiding.

Dani   Oh dear. I was only gone for a second. What happened?

Merga   My car!

Dani   Yes … Oh, someone has written on it.

Mamo   What does it say?

Dani   *[Reads loudly]* 'This man is a slaver! He steals boys and sells them!'

Merga   What nonsense. I am an honest businessman. I swear to God—

Mamo	*[Stands right in front of him]* 'God will punish this man! He will run but he will never escape from justice!' You don't remember me, do you, 'Uncle' Merga?
Merga	I've never seen you in my life.
Mamo	You don't remember kidnapping me from my house and selling me to that farmer in the countryside.
Merga	*[Recognizes him]* You. What are you doing here? *The boys surround him.* You've got this all wrong.
Million	Then explain to us.
Merga	I'll call the police.
Buffalo	And tell them what?
Merga	Look. I have money. *[Brings out his wallet]* How much do you want— *Million snatches the wallet out of his hand.*
Shoes	Your shoes. Take them off.
Getachew	You are waste. Scavenging from waste is not stealing, is it, Million?
Million	You heard him.
Merga	No. *Suri growls at Merga. He takes his shoes off.*
Buffalo	Your clothes.
Merga	Please.
Buffalo	Off! *Merga strips to his underwear.*
Million	Now run. And don't let us see you on the streets of Addis. Run!

Merga runs away. The boys laugh and jeer. Suri barks in triumph.

[Counts the money from Merga's wallet] Thirty birr!

Getachew	What do we do with it?
Million	PARTY!

They dance, sing and drink fizzy drinks. They have a great time.

Ato Mesfin appears. Paulos follows. He looks at the group of dancing street kids. He spots Dani, who is telling a story. Getachew and Mamo play sword fighting, kung fu-style.

Dani	Then the Kung Fu Hyena said, 'You talking to me?'
Paulos	Daniel?

The partying stops. Mamo drops his stick.

Dani	Father.
Paulos	Dani, is it really you?

Paulos steps forward, near where Mamo dropped his stick. Dani steps back. Suri grabs the stick and runs away with it.

Million and Buffalo step forward.

Million	Is this your father?
Dani	Yes.
Million	Who's the other guy?
Dani	Ato Mesfin, my Amharic teacher.
Buffalo	The guy who taught you to write stories?
Dani	Yes.
Million	Give me five.

Million high-fives Ato Mesfin. Paulos steps forward. Mamo, followed by the other boys, group protectively around Dani.

Dani	No.

Paulos	No? What do you mean 'no'? No what?
Dani	I'm not going to Feisal.
Paulos	Ridiculous. You can't have chosen to live like this, just because you—
Million	You heard Dani. He's not going.
Paulos	This is between me and my son. Who the hell are you?
Million	I'm his joviro.
Paulos	His what?
Million	His boss. He does what I tell him.
Mamo	No he doesn't. He does what he wants.
Ato Mesfin	Why don't we sit down and talk things over?
	The boys get crates to sit on.
	Well, Daniel, you've certainly managed to surprise us. I'd just like to say what an excellent story you wrote. *[To Mamo]* It was you who sold it to me?
Mamo	Yes.
Ato Mesfin	I've missed you in my class, Daniel. You are by far the most talented writer I've ever taught. I want to teach you again.
Dani	I'm no good in the other subjects.
Paulos	I'll get you a lesson teacher.
Ato Mesfin	I'm not sure if the school's the best place for you right now. Not just yet.
Paulos	Excuse me. I know what's best for my son.
Ato Mesfin	Please, sir. *[To Dani]* I've been talking to a couple of colleagues from another school. They've agreed to tutor you for a while, to bring you up to scratch in your other subjects. It would take a term or two. You could start back at school when you're ready. *[To Paulos]* I thought it would be best for Daniel to

decide for himself. *[To Dani]* Or if you prefer it, you could live with me while you get back on your feet.

Paulos	No! Please Daniel, come back home. I've missed you so much. Please come back with me now.
Dani	I don't know. I'd only disappoint you again. You'd get furious with me and send me off to Feisal.

Suri growls.

Million	What are you doing? Your old man is begging you to come back! Sir, if he doesn't want to go with you take me instead.
The Boys	Take me! Take me!
Paulos	Your mother is coming home tomorrow night. What do I tell her if you don't come home?
Dani	Mum? She's alive?
Paulos	I've spent the whole time lying to her about your whereabouts. I've never lied to her before.
Dani	But the funeral at the house. The sweets lady said—
Paulos	Oh, that was for your Uncle Asselefech. I let your cousins hold the reception in the garden. How did you …? She's fine. The operation was a total success.
Dani	She's fine.
Paulos	In the best health she's been for years.
Dani	*[Sobs]* She's fine.
Paulos	*[Holds Dani]* Now please say yes, you'll come home.

Pause. **Dani** *looks at the gang. They playfully threaten to beat him up.*

Dani	Yes.

The boys cheer. **Mamo** *smiles, sadly.*

Paulos	Now come on. You need a bath.

Dani *runs over to* **Mamo**.

Dani	I want Mamo to come home with us.
	Paulos looks horrified.
	He looked out for me. Without him I couldn't have survived.
Paulos	I'm sure your friend has family to look after him.
Mamo	You're right. They're right here. Go on, Dani. Take care.
	They hug each other. **Dani** *wipes the tears from his eyes.*
Mamo	We are survivors.
Dani	Survivors.
	Suri simpers.
	[Bends down and hugs her] Oh Suri.
Mamo	*[Bends down to join them]* I'll look after her for you. Go.
	Dani goes with Paulos and Ato Mesfin. He turns round to give one last wave to the boys and exits.
Getachew	*[To Mamo]* You idiot. You missed your chance.
Million	Our Dani's gone.
Buffalo	Just as I was beginning to like him.
Million	Buffalo!
Shoes	Ah! I should have asked his father for his shoes.
Getachew	You and your shoes.
Buffalo	What about you? I saw you angling for his wallet.
Getachew	That is a lie!
	Buffalo inspects Shoes' hand. It has swollen.
Million	After we scavenge, straight to the clinic. Mamo, sing us a song.
	Mamo looks away in Dani's direction.
Buffalo	You didn't seriously think he would take you with him, did you?

ACT 3   SCENE 9

91

Million	Buffalo . . .

*They leave **Mamo** alone. They go sifting through the rubbish heap.*

***Mamo** heaves with tears. **Suri** snaps at his feet, trying to get him to follow **Dani**. **Mamo** wipes his eyes dry and plays with **Suri**. He looks down and sees **Dani**'s notebook and pen. He picks them up. He puts them into his shirt and runs to join the gang sifting through the rubbish heap. He starts a rendition of* Survival. *The boys pick up the tune.*

Blackout

ACTIVITIES

● ●

ACTIVITIES

THE GARBAGE KING

Working in pairs, imagine that you are the joint directors of a theatre company. You have decided to stage a production of *The Garbage King*. You have set up a meeting with your actors to introduce them to the play.

You need to plan what you are going to say to your company and then make a short presentation.

Follow the steps below.

1.   Make notes about the setting of the play, explaining where it takes place. Start with the continent, then the country, then the capital city. Use the map below to help you.

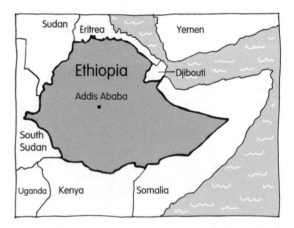

2.   Look at the information about street children. Decide which facts you will use to explain how street children live in Addis Ababa. Write a short paragraph to be included in your presentation to the actors.

It is estimated that up to half a million children live rough on the streets of Ethiopia's cities.

The children survive by begging, scavenging for food in bins, combing through rubbish to find things to sell, or doing small errands for people.

The children sleep on the streets, finding shelter in tunnels, sewers and drainage holes.

Many street children are orphans. Famine, violent conflict or diseases have killed their parents.

During periods of drought, many country people came into cities to find work and food.

Street children often form groups, share food and shelter, and try to help each other if they get sick.

Many children live and work on dumpsites all over the world. These young boys work on a dump near Jakarta, Indonesia.

3. Decide who the main characters are in the play, and how you will describe them to your actors. You might find it easiest to note key facts about each character in bullet points.

4. Choose what you think are the main themes of the play. Be prepared to explain how these themes are woven into the plot, and how you might convey them in your production of the play. You could include some of the themes below, or use your own ideas.

friendship

poverty/wealth

child labour

families

betrayal

survival

5. With your co-director, deliver a short presentation to your actors (your group or class). Decide beforehand who is going to say what. Be ready to answer questions from the actors afterwards!

If you have access to computers and time to do some research, you could use PowerPoint for your presentation and include some photographs of street children in Addis Ababa.

ASSESSMENT

● **Self-assessment.** Rate yourself out of three (with three being the highest score) for how well you did the following:
  ● worked with your co-director (including listening carefully to his or her ideas)
  ● planned your presentation
  ● delivered your presentation.

● **Peer assessment.** Ask 'the actors' to comment on two aspects of your presentation that you did well, and one aspect that could be improved.

2 MAMO AND DANI

The play opens with the meeting of Mamo and Dani in the cemetery. At first the boys appear very different, but they find they have a lot in common.

Get into pairs. One person from each pair should jot down all they know about Mamo, while the other notes down all they know about Dani from the play. Think about:

- appearance
- family background
- wealth/poverty
- age
- their possessions
- what has happened to them
- personality and character
- strengths and weaknesses
- hopes and fears.

If necessary, skim read parts of the playscript again to remind yourself about your character.

Now, as a pair, copy the Venn diagram below, making it as large as possible so you can write notes in it.

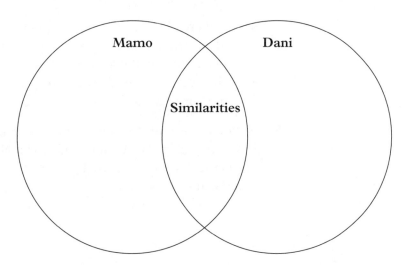

Add your notes and ideas about the characters into the diagram, talking about what information should go where.

First impressions

Re-read Act 1, Scene 1 in pairs, looking for evidence about what the boys first think of each other.

Then sit on the floor back to back. One partner should take on the role of Dani, the other Mamo. Take it in turns to say what you thought about the other boy, that first night, starting with 'When I first saw . . . I thought . . .'.

Final impressions

When you have finished reading the play, sit back to back with your partner again. Think carefully about what the boys think about each other at the end. Again, take turns to explain what you think about each other, starting with 'I hope . . . will always be my friend, even though . . .'.

Assessment

- **Self-assessment.** Consider how well you explored your character. Give yourself a thumbs up 👍 or thumbs down 👎 as to whether you:

    - gathered lots of information about your character
    - identified the similarities and differences between the two friends in the Venn diagram
    - showed a good understanding of the other character in your role play.

- **Teacher assessment.** Invite your teacher to comment on how well you spoke about the other character. Ask your teacher to comment on what you expressed well, and what you could improve on.

3   WHO'S WHO IN THE GANG?

In small groups, act out a scene with members of the street gang, without speaking (miming). Your audience will have to guess who is who in the street gang, using just visual clues, such as body language, gestures, expression and attitude.

Follow the steps below.

1. First decide who is going to take on which role in your group. Choose from:

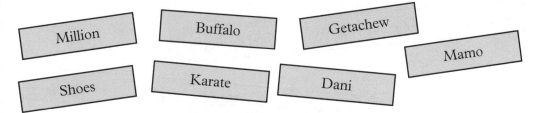

Million   Buffalo   Getachew   Mamo

Shoes   Karate   Dani

2. Each person in the group needs to think carefully about what they know about their character. If it helps, jot down some notes. You may want to refer back to the playscript to check out some details.

    Think about these questions:
    *   How old is my character?
    *   What is his position in the gang? How can I show this?
    *   What is his attitude towards the others?
    *   What sort of personality does he have and how can I show this?
    *   Does he have any special possessions, habits, interests?
    *   How might he stand/move? (Link this to how he might be feeling.)
    *   What sort of facial expressions would my character use, e.g. sullen, angry, vulnerable, sad, thoughtful, etc.?

3. In turn, share your thoughts with the rest of the group about each character. Listen carefully to other people's suggestions and ideas. Try out different looks and moves, helping each other to improve their role.

4. Create a new scene, or choose one from the playscript. Rehearse the scene, remembering that no words or sounds are allowed, so you will have to use your bodies and faces to make sure your audience know what is happening.

Here are some ideas:

The gang is picking out different items in the rubbish heap.

One member of the gang steals something.

The gang is begging and is given some food or money.

The gang is being chased by the police or another gang.

5. Perform your scene in front of the class, trying to convey your character through the way you move, look and interact with the other actors. At the end, ask the audience to guess who's who in the gang, and to give reasons for their answers. Also ask the audience to say what they think has happened in the scene.

ASSESSMENT

- **Self-assessment.** Rate yourself on a scale of 1 to 3 (with 3 being the highest score) as to how well you:
  - moved like your character
  - showed your character's personality
  - showed how your character felt about the others in the gang.

- **Peer assessment.** Ask the audience to give two positive comments about your group mime. Then ask for one suggestion to improve the scene.

4   PRIZED POSSESSIONS

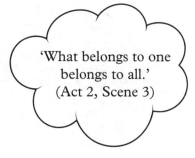

'What belongs to one
belongs to all.'
(Act 2, Scene 3)

This is one of the rules of the gang. It means that the contents
of Dani's bag are shared out among the boys.

1. In pairs, talk about:
    ● which items are given to whom
    ● the value of these items to their new owner, and how
       this is shown
    ● the significance of these items in the story (e.g. do
       any of them feature later in the story?).

2. In groups of three, imagine you are going to live rough on
    the streets. If you could take just two of your possessions
    with you, what would they be? Would they be for
    entertainment, for sentimental value, or for survival?

3. As a group, talk about your ideas and shortlist three items
    that you would take between you. Be prepared to explain
    why you chose these objects.

4. Share your ideas with the whole class, and try to agree on
    the top three items.

Remember, you will have no access to electricity on the
street and batteries will soon run out . . .

Key props

Look at these other items featured in the playscript:

5. In pairs, think about how these items are important in the story. How are they used and how do they affect the plot? How might the story be different without them?

6. Decide which are the most important in the story and which are the least important. Rank them in order, with the most important first and the least important at the end. Be prepared to justify your choices to the rest of the class.

News report

7. Imagine you are a news reporter who hears about the episode of the street boys and Merga's car. Write a brief report for the *Addis Ababa Times*.

   Remember to include:
   - a headline to hook the reader
   - a summary of events
   - details about who was involved
   - comments from some eye-witnesses
   - a picture (this can be just a quick sketch)
   - a caption to explain the picture
   - suggestions about any consequences (e.g. whether Merga is reported to the police or whether the boys are caught and punished, etc.).

Assessment

- **Self-assessment.** How well do you understand the significance of some objects in the story? Give yourself a thumbs up 👍 or thumbs down 👎 depending on whether you:
  - remembered who received each of Dani's possessions
  - recognized how important some items were to the story
  - worked well with your partner.

- **Teacher assessment.** Ask your teacher to choose one of the most interesting newspaper reports and to read it aloud. Ask your teacher to comment on why it is such an effective piece of writing.

5   DIFFICULT CHOICES

1. Many of the characters in *The Garbage King* have to make difficult choices. In pairs, list some of the difficult choices that the characters have to make throughout the play. Your list might start like this:

   1. Should Mamo take the job with his 'uncle'?
   2. Should Ruth go abroad for hospital treatment and leave Dani?
   3. Should Dani run away or stay and be sent to live with Feisal?

2. Choose one of the difficult choices that one of the characters makes. Explore that choice by drawing the character (it can be a very simple sketch) and placing thought bubbles on either side of the drawing. On one side, write reasons **for** the choice in the thought bubbles and on the other side, write reasons **against** the choice.

   For example:

I hate Feisal. He is cruel and will beat me.

If I stay, at least I'll have food and shelter.

I'll be better off on my own. My Dad hates me anyway.

My Mum will be upset if she hears I've run away.

My Mum might not ever come home again.

I don't know where I'd run away to. Will I survive on my own?

You might want to explore one of these choices:

> Million – should he accept Getachew back into the gang but punish him anyway because he broke the rules?

> Mamo – should Karate be left to die in hospital?

Write a diary entry

If your character could write, what might he say in his diary about his dilemma? Using the ideas in your thought bubbles, write a diary entry, weighing up the pros and cons of the decision.

Remember:
- A diary is written in the first person, so use the words 'I', 'we' and 'me'.
- Write in full, clear sentences, checking your punctuation and spelling.
- Explain the choice first, then go through the arguments for and against, then write your final conclusion (what you decide to do).
- You might find the following phrases useful:

'If I . . . then perhaps . . .'

'On the other hand. . .'

'I suppose there's a chance that. . .'

'Alternatively. . .'

'I wonder. . .'

'Right, I've decided that. . .'

Assessment

- **Self-assessment.** How well do you think you have understood your character's dilemma? Choose one of these answers:
  - Very well – I have explored the reasons for and against his/her choice.
  - Quite well – I have identified some of his/her ideas.
  - Not well – I need a bit more support to understand this.

- **Peer assessment.** Swap your diary entry with your partner. Read through and proof-read for spelling, punctuation and grammar errors. Mark any suggested changes in pencil and return it to your partner.

6 PREPARING FOR A PRODUCTION

In 2010 The Unicorn Theatre in London performed *The Garbage King*. A very special guest was flown in from Addis Ababa – a young man called Belete.

Elizabeth Laird (author of the novel *The Garbage King*) met Belete in Addis Ababa, when he was a street boy living rough with his friends and his dog, Suri. The story of Mamo is based on Belete's childhood. Belete now has a job and a home, and is learning to read and write English at night school.

Imagine you are staging a production of *The Garbage King*. In groups, plan and prepare some publicity materials to advertize your play. You will need to produce:

- a poster
- a short written programme
- a video clip.

1. Divide out the work between you, deciding who will work on what.
2. Plan your own part of the work carefully before discussing what you plan to do with the rest of the group.
3. Create your publicity materials, using the information in the text boxes to help you with each task.
4. Present your materials to the rest of the class.

Poster

Remember to include:
- the title
- author and playwright's name
- when and where the performance will take place
- a few sentences describing the play (picking out key features)
- an eye-catching picture or design.

Think carefully about the colours and design of your poster.

Programme

Remember to include:
- a title page
- a list of the cast members
- some background information about the author, the novel and the play
- a brief summary of each Act.

You might also want to include a charity appeal for money to help street children in Addis Ababa.

Video advert

You could record your advert on a mobile phone.

Remember to include:
- the title
- details of the performance (when and where)
- a summary of the setting and outline of key characters
- some of the key themes/messages of the play
- say who you think this play will appeal to and why

You might find it helpful to make notes and rehearse your video before you record it. Avoid lots of pauses, repetition, and informal phrases.

ASSESSMENT

- **Self-assessment.** Rate yourself on a scale of 1 to 3 (with 3 being the highest score) for how well you:
  - worked with your group (including listening carefully to other people's ideas and suggesting your own)
  - planned and discussed your project
  - created, checked and presented your publicity materials.

- **Peer assessment.** Ask another group to comment on two features of your publicity materials that they think are good, and one feature that could be improved.

7 WRITING A FINAL SCENE

In the novel, the story ends with Dani and Mamo meeting up three months after their parting, and spending the afternoon together.

Mamo was waiting for him outside the pastry shop where, months earlier, they had glimpsed each other for the first time. He was wearing a nearly-new sweatshirt and there were shoes on his feet. He smiled almost shyly as Dani came up to him.

'What's in that?' he said, looking at the bag that Dani was carrying over his shoulder. 'Not running away again are you?'

'Course not.' Dani led the way into the shop. 'Come on. I'll tell you later.'

In the novel, this is what happens in the final chapter:

The boys have cakes and a drink in the shop.

↓

Mamo tells Dani that he is living with Tiggist and Yacob, and they are expecting a baby. He is also going to night school.

↓

Dani tells Mamo that he is re-taking his year at school, but his father doesn't nag him too much because he is afraid that Dani will run away again.

↓

The boys go back to the gang's old pitch and find Suri guarding the gang's blankets.

↓

Mamo explains that Tiggist doesn't like dogs so Suri stayed with Million and the gang.

↓

Dani unzips his new bag and leaves some things for the gang: a few clothes, shoes and a bit of money.

↓

Mamo and Dani say goodbye.

In pairs, write another scene for the playscript, based on the final chapter of the book.

> Remember!
> - Lay out the new script with the actors' names on the left and their lines on the right.
> - Tell the story through direct speech (what the boys say to each other).
> - Use stage directions to show what the actors do.

When you have finished your first draft of the new scene, try to act it out. Check whether:

- the words seem natural and right for the two characters
- the boys listen and respond to each other
- you have included stage directions.

Make amends to improve your first draft, then write out the final version. Give it to another pair to act out.

ASSESSMENT

- **Self-assessment.** Think carefully about how well you worked on your new script. Give yourself a thumbs up 👍 or thumbs down 👎 as to whether you did the following:

- included all the events listed on pages 109–110
- worked well with your partner
- revised your draft to make improvements.

- **Peer assessment.** Ask the pair who tried out your new

  scene to comment on two aspects of it that they felt were good, and one aspect that could be improved.

FURTHER ACTIVITIES

1. Mamo sings Bob Marley's song 'Survival' at the start and end of the play. Find this song and listen to the words. How does it link to the themes of this play?

2. Dani's teacher says that 'Dani is very good at telling stories'. Repeat the story that Dani begins, *The Wicked Hyena*, and then make up your own middle and ending for it. Remember that it was intended to comfort Karate, so make sure it has a happy ending.

3. Do some research about the author of the novel, Elizabeth Laird. Find out about her life and some of her other books. Use the information to create a mini-presentation for the rest of the class. You may find the author's own website helpful.

4. If you were a millionaire and wanted to help the street children in Addis Ababa, what would you do? Try to think of ways of helping them long term, not just giving them food and shelter now.

5. Imagine you are a gang leader, living on the streets. What rules would you have for your gang? If anyone broke the rules, what would you do? Try to be fair and make the safety and well-being of the gang your top priority.

6. Write a ten-question quiz to test your partner's knowledge about the play. Include questions about its setting, some of the characters and the plot.